Success
Assessment Papers

More English

age 10 – 11 · levels 4 – 5

Alison Head

Sample page

clear instructional text

level showing attainment target

paper number for quick reference

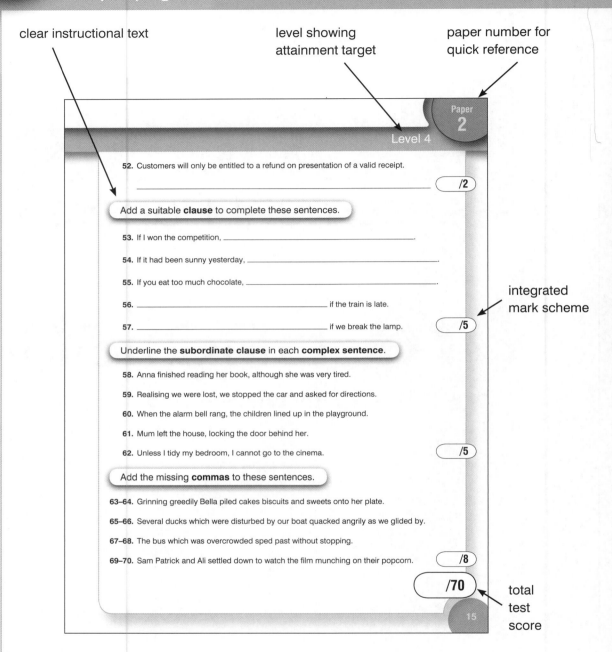

Paper
2

Level 4

52. Customers will only be entitled to a refund on presentation of a valid receipt.

_____ /2

Add a suitable **clause** to complete these sentences.

53. If I won the competition, _____.

54. If it had been sunny yesterday, _____.

55. If you eat too much chocolate, _____.

56. _____ if the train is late.

57. _____ if we break the lamp. /5

Underline the **subordinate clause** in each **complex sentence**.

58. Anna finished reading her book, although she was very tired.

59. Realising we were lost, we stopped the car and asked for directions.

60. When the alarm bell rang, the children lined up in the playground.

61. Mum left the house, locking the door behind her.

62. Unless I tidy my bedroom, I cannot go to the cinema. /5

Add the missing **commas** to these sentences.

63–64. Grinning greedily Bella piled cakes biscuits and sweets onto her plate.

65–66. Several ducks which were disturbed by our boat quacked angrily as we glided by.

67–68. The bus which was overcrowded sped past without stopping.

69–70. Sam Patrick and Ali settled down to watch the film munching on their popcorn. /8

/70

15

integrated mark scheme

total test score

Contents

PAPER 1

It was the day of the school's annual treasure hunt. Miss Smart had hidden clues all over the village and the children would race each other to collect the clues and find the treasure. Sam had been bragging all week about how fast he was and Billy was sick of it.

As soon as the whistle started the race, Billy was off like a rocket. He had already cracked the first clue they had been given at school and he headed for the river bank to find the second one. Looking over his shoulder, he saw that Sam was still some way behind. Sam would hate losing to Billy and the thought of it made Billy smile.   5

At the river bank, Billy looked frantically for the clue. He saw nothing at first but then caught sight of a scrap of paper caught on a branch halfway down the bank. It must have been dislodged by the rain the previous night. Billy slithered down the bank and reached out for   10
the paper. He had just managed to grasp it between his fingertips when the bank gave way and Billy found himself sliding towards the water. The river was swollen with rainwater from the storm and Billy could see that it was deep and moving fast. If he ended up in the water, he knew he would be swept away. Scrabbling about him, he grabbed a tree root that had been exposed by the mudslide on the bank.   15

Suddenly a face appeared above Billy. It was Sam. "Billy, are you OK?" he asked, apparently concerned.

"The bank collapsed," replied Billy. "I'm stuck. Go and get help!"

"It's OK," replied Sam. "I think I can reach you. Pass me the clue and then I'll pull you up."

Billy didn't trust Sam, but the tree root he clung to did not look very strong. Reluctantly, he   20
reached up with the clue, then waited for Sam to take his hand and pull him up the bank. Sam smiled down at Billy.

"Thanks, Billy Boy," he sneered, and disappeared.

At that moment, the tree root snapped and Billy plunged into the swirling water. The current pulled him under, but he struggled to the surface and tried to swim to the edge. He could   25
see a ledge ahead and thought that if he could only reach it, he might clamber onto it and wait for help to arrive. The water was cold and full of debris and tree branches but Billy slowly made his way towards the ledge and scrambled out of the water. Once on the ledge, Billy could see that this part of the bank had collapsed too, bringing a tree down with it. Shivering, Billy wondered if he would be able to climb up the fallen tree, to the top of the   30
bank. He had been carried some distance by the river and he wondered where he was.

Taking a closer look at the tree, Billy was surprised to see a wooden box hidden among the roots. The box had his school logo on its lid and suddenly Billy knew what it was. It was the treasure! It must have been hidden under the tree the day before, and washed down the bank when it collapsed. Smiling, Billy tucked the box inside his coat and climbed carefully   35
up the fallen tree. He had beaten Sam after all!

Underline your answers.

1. How often did Billy's school hold the treasure hunt?

once a month   once a term   once a year   this is the first time

2. Where does Billy go to school?

on a farm   in a village   in a town   in a city

3. What had Sam done that annoyed Billy?

He found the treasure.   He kept saying how fast he was.

He said Billy would win the treasure hunt.   He was faster than Billy.

4. Which word is closest in meaning to the word "bragging" (line 3)?

arguing   lying   boasting   laughing

5. What do you think the **phrase** "Billy was off like a rocket" means (line 4)?

He exploded.   He was very fast.   He jumped very high.   He was dangerous.

6. Billy "cracked" the first clue (line 4). What do you think this means?

broke   solved   lost   gave away

7. Why do you think Billy smiled (line 7)?

He was winning.   He had found the second clue.

Sam really wanted to find the treasure before Billy.   Billy had found the treasure.

8. Where were the children given the first clue?

at the school   on the river bank   in the river   in the village

9. What had the weather been like the night before the treasure hunt?

frosty   windy   rainy   warm

10. On what was the second clue caught?

a tree root   debris   a tree branch   the river bank

11. Why does Billy think the second clue is where he finds it?

Sam put it there.   Miss Smart hid it there.

It is not really a clue.   The rain dislodged it.

12. Underline the statement that is true about the second clue.

Sam finds the clue.

Billy finds the clue, then the river bank collapses.

Billy finds the clue because the river bank collapses.

Billy loses the clue when the river bank collapses.

/12

Answer these questions.

13–14. Find and write down two **verbs** that show that Billy struggled to stop himself slipping into the water (line 14).

_____ _____

15. Which word has a similar meaning to "swollen" (line 12)? Underline your answer.

gushing   cold   dirty   bloated

16. How did Billy know he would be swept away if he fell in the water? Underline your answer.

The water was cold and full of debris.   The river bank had collapsed.

The water was deep and flowing fast.   It was raining.

17. When Sam sees Billy on the river bank, do you think he is really "concerned" (line 17)? Give a reason for your answer.

_____

18. Why did Billy decide to pass the clue to Sam?

_____

19. Underline the word closest in meaning to "sneered" (line 23).

mocked   cautioned   comforted   wished

20. Do you think Sam went for help after he left Billy on the river bank? Give a reason for your answer.

_____

21. Underline the word closest in meaning to "debris" (line 27).

desperate   litter   clamber   reeds

22. Once Billy is safely on the ledge, what does he plan to do? Underline your answer.

wait for Sam to come back   climb the fallen tree to the top of the bank

look for the clue   wonder where he is

23. Explain why you think Billy realises that the wooden box is the treasure he is looking for.

_____

24. How does Billy think the treasure came to be on the ledge?

_____

25. Although Billy did not find all the clues, he did find the treasure. Do you think this is fair? Give a reason for your answer.

_____   /13

Underline the **preposition** in each **sentence**.

26. The cat squeezed between the fence posts.

27. We went to the station and caught the train.

28. Dad made a cheese sandwich for me.

29. We heard a noise behind the door.

30. Inside the box was a beautiful ring.

31. A sign over the door said "Closed".   /6

Tick the sentences that contain an **active verb**.

32. They were soaked by the rain.

33. Jade bought some chocolate in the shop.

34. Matthew scored the winning goal.

35. The vase was broken.

36. The baby birds were fed by their mother.

37. Our car was repaired at the garage.

38. Mrs Black takes her dog for a walk every day.

39. The teacher handed out the books.

/8

Choose a sentence ending so each sentence makes sense. Draw lines to match up the pairs.

40. If it is sunny,   he would be angry.

41. If you are not careful,   I would read the whole book.

42. If I had more time,   I will put on sunscreen.

43. If she had been earlier,   we will win the trophy.

44. If Dad was here,   you could fall.

45. If we win the match,   she would have caught the bus.

/6

Add the missing commas to these sentences.

46–47. We could still see the ball even though it was late so we played another game.

48–49. At the cinema Mum said we could have popcorn drinks and ice-cream!

50–51. We ran down the path jumping over the rocks to the beach.

52–53. It was a beautiful day when giggling happily the girls ran out to play.

/8

Add a **main clause** to make a **complex sentence**. Remember to add the correct **punctuation**.

54. When it began to rain _____

55. Although she tried hard _____

56. Unless we hurry _____

57. Covered in dust _____

58. Swinging through the trees _____

59. Blowing out the candles _____

60. Arriving late _____ /7

> ## Underline the spelling mistake in each sentence.

61. In the medow, a flock of sheep were grazing.

62. The bride wore a beutiful white dress.

63. While we were waching the football match, it began to rain.

64. The scientist was working on a new chemical formular.

65. I ment to bring my book home but I forgot.

66. The reelistic special effects in the film were amazing.

67. The teacher gave Mark top marks for his excelent story. /7

> ## Write these sentences again, using **direct speech**.

68. Mum said we needed to tidy our bedrooms.

_____

69. Miss Miles explained that we would have a maths test tomorrow.

_____

70. Ben grumbled that he was hungry and tired.

_____

_____ /3

/70

PAPER 2

How to make a birdfeeder

Turn an old, plastic bottle into a birdfeeder and encourage wild birds into your garden! This environmentally friendly project is simple to do, but be sure to ask an adult for a helping hand where you see this symbol.

You will need: 5
- a clean, 1-litre plastic bottle with its lid
- a sturdy twig (about as thick as a pencil and around 20cm long)
- a whiteboard marker pen
- a craft knife
- string for hanging up the feeder   10
- 1kg of mixed birdseed.

1. Start by drawing a small cross on the side of the bottle, about 3cm from the bottom. Opposite this cross, draw another one.
2. Use the tip of a craft knife to pierce holes where you have marked the crosses on the bottle. Push your twig right through the bottle so that a short length is sticking out   15 from each side of the bottle.
3. Make a small V-shaped cut about 4cm above each of the holes you have just made.
4. Bend each of these cut out areas upwards, so they form a little roof over the V-shaped opening on each side of the bottle.   20
5. Use the tip of the craft knife to punch two small holes in the neck of the bottle.
6. Fill the feeder with mixed birdseed and replace the lid.
7. Thread string through the holes. Hang your feeder from a tree.
8. Remember to refill your feeder when it is empty. This is especially important in the cold 25 winter months when alternative food supplies are scarce. You should also make sure there is always a supply of fresh drinking water available and that it is not allowed to freeze in winter.

Be bird-safe! If cats or other predators visit your garden, think carefully about where you hang your feeder. Position it away from fences and walls. Some birdseed will also fall to   30 the ground, so make sure you hang your feeder where birds on the ground will have a clear view of predators approaching.

> Answer these questions.

1–2. Suggest two reasons why the birdfeeder is "environmentally friendly" (line 2).

_____

_____

3. Why do you think the instructions ask children to get an adult to help them with some parts of the project?

_____

4. Suggest why the feeder should be made from a "clean" soft drinks bottle (line 6).

_____

5. Which of these words is closest in meaning to the word "sturdy" (line 7)? Underline your answer.

hard   robust   long   brown

6. What is the whiteboard marker used for in this project?

_____

7–8. Find and write down two words that are used to describe making a hole in something.

_____   _____

9. What is the "neck" of a bottle (line 21)?

_____

10. What does the word "thread" mean, as it is used in line 24?

_____

11. What does the word "scarce" mean? (line 26)? Underline your answer.

scary   dangerous   limited   abundant

12. The text mentions birds' "alternative food supplies" (line 26). Suggest another food supply for birds.

_____

13. Why might this source of food not be available during the winter?

_____

14. What do you think "Be bird-safe!" (line 29) means in this text? Tick your answer.

Stay safe from dangerous wild birds.

Lock the birdfeeder up at night.

Think about the safety of birds when positioning the birdfeeder.

Make sure wild birds have enough to eat.

15. What does the word "predator" mean (line 29)? Underline your answer.

an animal that is kept as a pet   an animal that eats another animal

an animal that is eaten by another animal   a bird that is eaten by a cat

16. Suggest why the feeder should be hung "away from fences and walls".

_____

17. What will happen to the seed that falls to the ground?

_____

18–19. Imperative verbs are **verbs** that tell you what to do. Find and write down two imperative verbs.

_____   _____

20–22. Draw lines to join up the features on the left with the correct description of how they are used in this text.

Bullet points are used to   highlight important extra information.

Numbered points are used to   list the things you will need for the project.

The text box is used to   list what you need to do, in order.

23. Describe how birds can use the feeder.

_____

24. Which of these lengths is *not* mentioned anywhere in the text? Underline your answer.

20cm   3m   4cm   3cm

25. Has this text convinced you that making a birdfeeder is a good way to help wild birds? Give a reason for your answer.

_____   /25

> Underline two spelling mistakes in each **sentence**.

26–27. I coud not decide whitch shoes to buy.

28–29. Eating friut and vegetables is helthy for you.

30–31. A warty toud lept into the water.

32–33. Dad caried my little brother on his sholders.   /8

> Write these sentences again, so they make sense.

34. I rides a pony at weekends.

_____

35. The girls ran for the bus but them missed it.

_____

36. Although it was raining, Jack and Tim finish their game.

_____

37. My dogs loves to play with their toys.

_____

38. I was so full, I could not eat nothing else.

_____ /5

> Add a suitable **preposition** to complete each sentence.

39. The cat squeezed _____ the gap in the fence.

40. I eventually found my phone _____ my bed.

41. The man _____ us in the queue was rude and impatient.

42. Dad hung the picture _____ the fireplace.

43. Kate baked a cake _____ her brother's birthday party. /5

> Add **speech marks** to these sentences.

44. Hurry up! Mum shouted down the stairs.

45. I'll see you later, said Jill as she left the house.

46. Don't forget to do your homework, reminded Miss Smith.

47. Josh asked, Do I have time to make a snack?

48. It looks as if it could rain, observed Joe.

49. Remember your lunch money, said Dad.

50. Tara giggled, That tickles! /7

> Write these sentences again, using less formal English.

51. Winners will be notified in writing no more than eight working days after the competition closes.

_____

_____

52. Customers will only be entitled to a refund on presentation of a valid receipt.

_____ /2

Add a suitable **clause** to complete these sentences.

53. If I won the competition, _____.

54. If it had been sunny yesterday, _____.

55. If you eat too much chocolate, _____.

56. _____ if the train is late.

57. _____ if we break the lamp.   /5

Underline the **subordinate clause** in each **complex sentence**.

58. Anna finished reading her book, although she was very tired.

59. Realising we were lost, we stopped the car and asked for directions.

60. When the alarm bell rang, the children lined up in the playground.

61. Mum left the house, locking the door behind her.

62. Unless I tidy my bedroom, I cannot go to the cinema.   /5

Add the missing **commas** to these sentences.

63–64. Grinning greedily Bella piled cakes biscuits and sweets onto her plate.

65–66. Several ducks which were disturbed by our boat quacked angrily as we glided by.

67–68. The bus which was overcrowded sped past without stopping.

69–70. Sam Patrick and Ali settled down to watch the film munching on their popcorn.   /8

/70

PAPER 3

Stride, don't ride!
Walking to school is good for the environment and good for you too!

With growing congestion on our roads and rising obesity rates in the UK, walking to school is one small solution to a great big problem! That's why we are making next month, March, national "March to school month". We are challenging schoolchildren and their parents up and down the UK to leave the car at home and walk to school instead.   5

So what's in it for you? The number of children being driven to school has risen sharply over the last 20 years. All of those extra cars on the road means more waiting in queues and more pollution in the air. By leaving the car at home and walking instead, you will be doing your bit to reduce pollution and make the roads around schools that bit safer too. You'll also be   10
saving your parents money, because fewer miles on the road means a smaller petrol bill and fewer costly car repairs.

You will be doing your health good, too. Developing a lifelong walking habit now will keep you fit and healthy today, and in the long term it can help to protect you from obesity, heart disease and stroke when you are older.   15

Young people between the ages of seven and 11 should be active for around an hour each day in order to stay healthy. Walking to and from school is the perfect way to become more active. You will find you arrive at school wide awake and ready to learn, as well as getting to spend time on the way chatting to your parents or friends! Sarah Price, 11, began walking to school a year ago, after her parents decided she was old enough to cross the roads safely.   20
She walks with a group of friends and looks forward to their time together. "Walking to school gives us a chance to share all our news before we get into the classroom, so we are less likely to chat during lessons!" she says.

Local government initiatives across the country are improving safety for pedestrians, especially around schools, with new crossings, traffic calming measures and crossing patrols outside a   25
growing number of schools. After last year's campaign successfully encouraged more of its pupils to walk to school, St Mary's School in Seamouth approached the local council and now has its very own Lollipop Lady. Head Teacher Mrs Parks says, "I can understand why some parents are worried about their children walking to school as this road is very busy in the mornings. Knowing they have a safe place to cross has made a huge difference to the number   30
of children choosing to walk, and that is good news for everybody."

Think you live too far from school to be able to walk? Why not ask your parents to drive you half way to school and walk the rest? You'll still be getting exercise and reducing pollution and who knows, you might find that after a few weeks you'll be able to walk all the way!

Look out for posters and fliers at your school soon. There will also be badges and goody   35
bags for children who make the commitment to striding, rather than riding, to school.

Underline your answers.

1. What does the word "congestion" (line 3) mean?

pollution   overcrowding   danger   accidents

2. What does the word "obesity" (line 3) mean?

being underweight   being overweight   suffering from asthma   being overcrowded

3. During which month was this article published?

March   January   February   April

4. Which **phrase** is closest in meaning to "challenging", as it is used in line 5?

arguing with   calling for   dreaming of   fighting with   /4

Answer these questions.

5–6. Find and write down two words in the text with a similar meaning to the word 'walk'.

_____   _____

7–8. Suggest two reasons why more children are being driven to school now than 20 years ago.

_____

_____

9–10. Apart from helping to prevent obesity, list two other long-term health benefits of walking.

_____

_____

11–13. As well as the health benefits, the text describes several other types of benefits of walking rather than driving. Give one example of each type in the chart.

environmental benefit	
economic benefit	
social benefit	

14. Of all the benefits of walking described in the text, which do you find most persuasive? Give a reason for your answer.

_____

_____

15–16. Find two reasons suggested in the text why schools might prefer children to walk to school rather than be driven.

_____

_____

17. What effect does "traffic calming" (line 25) have on how roads are used? Underline your answer.

reduces road rage   reduces congestion

reduces pedestrians   reduces the speed of the traffic

18–19. Find and write down two ways the campaign will be publicised in schools.

_____

_____

20. What is a "flier", as the word is used in line 35? Underline your answer.

a pilot   a helium-filled publicity balloon

a small publicity leaflet   a publicity flag

21. Think about the heading "Stride, don't ride". Why do you think the writer chose those words?

_____

_____

22. Think about the phrase "March to school month". Why do you think this name was chosen for the campaign?

_____

_____

23. Find one fact in the text.

_____

24. Find one opinion in the text.

_____

25. The writer has used questions in lines 32 and 33. Why do you think they have done this?

_____

_____ /21

> Write down the correct spelling for each of these words.

26. strainger _____

27. consert _____

28. obvius _____

29. concreat _____

30. deaper _____

31. villidge _____

32. pention _____

/7

> These **sentences** contain **passive verbs**.
> Write them again, using **active verbs**.

33. The letter was written by my aunt.

_____

34. Billy was chased by a big dog.

_____

35. Our house was built by a local builder.

_____

36. Their picnic was ruined by wasps.

_____

37. The best picture was painted by Eve.

_____

38. The plane was flown by an experienced pilot.

_____

39. My guitar was tuned by my music teacher.

_____ /7

Add a suitable **connective** to complete each sentence.

40. _____ Beth had a sore knee, she still won the race.

41. We waited at school _____ Mum arrived to collect us.

42. You will be cold _____ you wear a coat.

43. Our teacher will be pleased _____ we do well in our test.

44. I like football _____ I don't like cricket.

45. The smoke alarm went off _____ I burnt my toast.

46. Mum wrapped the present carefully, _____ she hid it in the cupboard. /7

Rewrite this short text using language that would be appropriate for a young child learning to read.

47–49. The exquisite butterfly landed on an azure bloom. Its wings blazed in the radiant sunshine. A bird warbled from the boughs of an adjacent tree.

_____

_____

_____

_____ /3

Add **semi-colons** to these sentences.

50. Freddie is learning to play the drums I feel sorry for his neighbours.

51. Claire is my best friend she can always make me smile.

52. Learning to swim is very important it could save your life one day.

53. My dog is really naughty she never does what she is told.

54. Ask me tomorrow I will give you my answer then.

55. She was very careful she did not make a single mistake.

56. I have pen-pals in Sydney, Australia Tokyo, Japan and Paris, France. /7

Add a suitable **main clause** to complete each sentence.

57. Until the show starts, _____.

58. Although I am not very good at it, _____.

59. When it stopped raining, _____.

60. If we tidy up quickly, _____.

61. _____, because he was angry.

62. _____, when the tide came in.

/6

Add all of the missing **punctuation** to these sentences.

63–65. Although Toms party was fantastic I was so tired afterwards

66–67. My uncle who lives in Switzerland sent me Swiss chocolates for my birthday.

68–70. My diary games and mobile phone which are my favourite things were packed away
carefully.

/8

/70

PAPER 4

Dear Diary,

Today was our school trip to Felton Heights theme park. I hardly slept a wink last night, which was probably a good thing because we had to be at school at 7.30 this morning! Ben Ross overslept so he didn't arrive until eight o'clock. Everyone was shouting and jeering when he got on the coach, just as the doors were closing, especially when they realised he was still wearing his pyjamas under his clothes! He must have felt really hot.

5

Once we were out of the town the journey wasn't too bad, even though it took a long time. There was a bit of a queue on the motorway so at ten o'clock the driver stopped at a service station so we could have a break, and by the time we got back on the motorway the queue had gone. Unfortunately, after we had been back on the road for about ten minutes, Charlotte realised she had left her purse at the service station when she had taken it out to buy a souvenir. She was livid when the driver wouldn't go back for it and complained noisily about him for the rest of the journey. She really got on my nerves, especially because when we finally got off the coach at the theme park, it turned out she had been sitting on her purse all along!

10

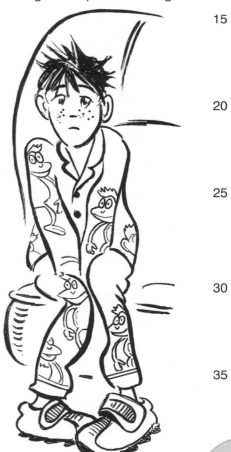

Picking the first ride to go on was really hard because they all looked so good. Some of the roller coasters were so tall I was too scared to go on them, so I told Charlotte I thought the queues were too long. We went on a couple of smaller roller coasters and then we plucked up the courage to try the log flume. We got soaked, but luckily it was sunny again today so our clothes dried really quickly. In the end we decided to go on a really tall roller coaster. It turns out that waiting in the queue was scarier than actually going on the ride, because we were there for half an hour getting more and more nervous. After that, the ride itself went so fast it was over before you knew it. All the same, we didn't want to do it again!

15

20

25

We were really sorry when it was time to go back to the coach to go home. Ben was late – again! At last he turned up, but the coach driver wouldn't let him get on the coach because his clothes were so wet from the log flume ride. Luckily he was still wearing his pyjamas underneath, so in the end, he had to take his top clothes off and ride all the way home in his PJs. Imagine how embarrassed he must have been. Late for the coach twice in one day and having to sit in his monkey jim-jams all the way home!

30

35

It was the best school trip I've ever been on. I can't wait to go back again!

Underline your answers.

1. What time did the coach leave the school?

7.30am   7.30pm   8am   10am

2. Why do you think the coach planned to leave so early in the morning?

to get the children out of bed early

because the children were excited about the trip

because it takes quite a long time to get to the theme park

because there was a queue on the motorway

3. Why do you think the writer of this text found it hard to sleep the night before?

She was waiting for the coach.   She was excited about the school trip.

She was worrying about her homework.   She was scared of the tallest roller coasters.

4. Which of these words has a similar meaning to "jeering" (line 4)?

smiling   mocking   criticising   gossiping

5. Which of these words has a similar meaning to the word "livid", as it is used in line 12?

upset   furious   worried   afraid

6. Why did Charlotte complain so loudly?

She had lost her purse at the service station.   She had bought a souvenir.

The coach driver wouldn't go back for the purse.   She was sitting on her purse.

7. Which of these words is most similar in meaning to "souvenir" (line 12)?

snack   keepsake   magazine   camera   /7

Answer these questions.

8. Do you think the driver was unreasonable in not going back for Charlotte's purse? Give a reason for your answer.

_____

9–10. Two types of queue are mentioned in the text. What are they?

_____   _____

11. Why do you think the writer told Charlotte that the queues for the tallest roller coasters were too long?

_____

12–13. Find and write down two words with a similar meaning to "afraid".

_____   _____

14. What kind of ride do you think a log flume is? Give a reason for your answer.

_____

15. Explain *in your own words* why the writer found queuing for the tall roller coaster more frightening than the ride itself.

_____

16–18. Find and write down three time **connectives** used in the text.

_____   _____   _____

19. What time of year do you think the school trip took place? Give a reason for your answer.

_____

20–21. Find and write down two informal ways for naming pyjamas.

_____   _____

22. Why do you think the writer chooses to use this kind of informal language?

_____

23. Read this **sentence**: "Imagine how embarrassed he must have been." (lines 34–35).
Why do you think the writer wrote this?

_____

24. Why do you think some people keep a diary?

_____

25. Imagine the diary entry that Ben Ross would write for the day of the school trip.
Write the first line of his diary entry.

_____ /18

Underline the correctly spelt word in each group.

26.	leasure	leisure	lessure	**27.**	cerial	cierial	cereal
28.	grannit	granate	granite	**29.**	sheperd	shepherd	shephard
30.	tortose	tortoise	tortuous	**31.**	fossil	fossle	fostle
32.	occation	occashion	occasion				

/7

Write these sentences again, reordering the words and adding
punctuation where necessary so that they make sense.

33–34. The bus arrived and we all piled eventually on.

_____

35–36. You do your homework unless you will get into trouble.

_____

37–38. The witch stirred cackling creepily the cauldron.

_____

39–40. Strawberries are served delicious at room temperature.

_____ /8

> Add an interesting **verb** in the past **tense** to complete each sentence.

41. The boys _____ over the wall and disappeared.

42. A flock of birds _____ across the sky.

43. Turning haughtily on her heel, she _____ out of the room.

44. With a flourish, the artist _____ his brush across the canvas.

45. Enjoying the warm morning sunshine, Abbie _____ slowly to school.

46. Kate _____ her reflection in the mirror.

47. Knife flashing, the chef quickly _____ the vegetables.

48. Excited, she _____ at the colourful wrapping paper on the gift. /8

> Add the missing **comma** to each sentence.

49. Counting on her fingers Amy solved the tricky maths problem.

50. Leaving a trail of muddy paw-prints behind him Prince headed for the sofa.

51. Although she was late Kate did not hurry.

52. Peering through the fog we made our way home.

53. Whenever Gran comes to stay she always brings us presents.

54. Licking its lips the cat watched the goldfish glide around its tank.

55. Andy ran down the path and out into the street leaving the gate wide open. /7

Replace each word in *italics* with a stronger word to make the statement more likely to be true.

56. With extra training I *might* _____ beat my record.

57. It *often* _____ snows during January.

58. To be sure that I get to school on time, I *should* _____ leave home by 8.30.

59. Look at the chocolate around his mouth; he *may* _____ have eaten the cake.

60. The most expensive phone *could* _____ be the best.

61. Dad *usually* _____ gets home from work before 6pm.

/6

Add a suitable word or **phrase** to complete the **personification** in each sentence.

62. Yellow daffodils _____ among the fresh spring grass.

63. Shadows _____ across the dusty floor of the cave.

64. A cool breeze _____ through the branches of the trees.

/3

Underline the **connective** word or phrase in each sentence.

65. Mark took another biscuit, although Mum had said no.

66. After we had finished washing the car, it started to rain.

67. Greg chose pizza but I chose pasta.

68. We finished the snowman, despite the cold.

69. In addition to painting the walls of my room, we have ordered new carpets.

70. We won't miss any of the film as long as the bus comes soon.

/6

/70

PAPER 5

The monkey and the bear

A mighty bear was travelling through a great forest when he strayed off the path, convinced he could find a shorter way out of the trees. Time passed and, reluctant to admit his mistake, the bear pressed on through the undergrowth, becoming more and more lost.

As he wandered about looking for a track to follow, he was eventually joined by a tiny monkey who swung through the branches above him, chattering away. Bear, absorbed in searching for a way out of the forest and dismissive of such a tiny creature, ignored his companion.

"I think you need my help," said Monkey, finally.

"Don't be ridiculous!" stormed Bear. "How could a tiny thing like you help a powerful bear like me? Why, you're so small you would fit in one of my paws!" The bear raised a huge paw and flashed its sharp claws at the monkey, who darted into the trees and disappeared. Bear chuckled and continued on his way, confident that he would shortly find a track that would lead him directly out of the forest.

Darkness fell and still the bear wandered in circles through the forest, with no idea where he was or what direction he was walking in. Although he tramped many miles that night, sunrise saw him back where he had started, tired, hungry and even grumpier than usual. He sat on a fallen tree and fumed, wondering how a mere forest could outsmart a mighty creature like him.

"I think you need my help," piped a little voice in the branches above.

"Monkey, I thought we settled this yesterday," growled Bear, through gritted teeth. "You are no bigger than a pomegranate. I am the biggest animal in this forest. I could tear down that tree if I wanted to!" roared Bear, pointing to the tallest tree in the forest, in which Monkey sat. "How could you possibly help me?"

"It is true that I am small," said Monkey, "and I could no more tear down this tree than fly to the Moon. But I am the best climber in the forest. From the top of this tree I bet I could see everything… the path out of the forest, for example." Monkey's eyes twinkled. "I think you need my help," he repeated.

Bear considered his sore feet and rumbling stomach. In an instant, he realised how foolish he had been. Humbled, he said, "Monkey, I think I need your help. Please."

5

10

15

20

25

Underline your answers.

1. What kind of text is this?

a recount   a legend   a fable   science fiction

2. Which word best describes Bear's attitude for most of the story?

arrogant   afraid   worried   suspicious

3. What is a "pomegranate" (line 20)?

a fruit   a pebble   a flower   a vegetable

4. As it is used in line 11, which of these words is most similar in meaning to "flashed"?

flickered   displayed   shook   scratched

5. As it is used in line 11, which of these words is most similar in meaning to "darted"?

speared   thrown   dashed   whistled   **/5**

Answer these questions.

6. What is the moral of this story? Tick your answer.

The grass is always greener on the other side of the fence.

Even the smallest among us has something to offer.

Beauty is in the eye of the beholder.

Slow and steady wins the race.

7–8. Find and write down two **verbs** that show how angrily Bear speaks.

_____   _____

9–10. Find and write down two ways in which Bear describes how small Monkey is.

_____

_____

11. Why do you think Bear flashes his claws at Monkey?

_____

_____

12. Why do you think Bear chuckles when Monkey disappears into the trees after Bear has flashed his claws at him?

_____

_____

13. Why do you think Bear wanders in circles all night?

_____

_____

14–15. Find and write down two **comparative adjectives** in the text.

_____   _____

16–17. Find and write down two **superlative adjectives** in the text.

_____   _____

18. What kind of mood is Bear usually in? How do you know this?

_____

19. What reason does Bear give for thinking that Monkey would not be able to help him?

_____

20. In what way does Bear say that he could demonstrate his strength?

_____

21. Why does Monkey talk about not being able to fly to the Moon?

_____

22. Do you think Bear deserved Monkey's help? Give a reason for your answer.

_____

23. Why do you think Monkey's eyes twinkle (line 25)?

_____

24. Why do you think the writer repeats Monkey's words "I think you need my help" three times?

_____

25. In the final line of the story, Bear says "Please". What does this tell you about how his attitude towards Monkey has changed?

_____ /20

> ## Write down the **plural** of each of these **nouns**.

26. treaty   _____

27. child   _____

28. ox   _____

29. cactus   _____

30. aircraft   _____

31. tomato   _____

32. varnish   _____ /7

> ## Add a suitable **adverb** to complete each **sentence**.

33. _____, the cat stalked the blackbird.

34. _____, Dad picked up my sleepy baby sister.

35. _____, the door flew open and a strange woman walked in.

36. _____, the shop did not have the shoes I wanted in my size.

37. _____, the journey was over and we arrived.

38. _____, I had just enough money for the bus fare home.

39. _____, he eyed the cakes in the shop window.

/7

> Use the *italic* **connective** words and **phrases** to help you complete these sentences.

40. *Despite* the weight of her suitcase, _____.

41. Our team won the quiz *as a result of* _____.

42. I had planned to go swimming *but* _____.

43. *Whenever* I take my dog for a walk, _____.

44. *As* I was already late, _____.

45. He knew he was in trouble *when* _____.

46. *While* I was shopping in town, _____.

/7

> Write these sentences again, correcting the **punctuation**.

47–48. Although, she was annoyed Mum could still see the funny side.

_____

49–50. I ordered an ice-cream despite feeling really, full.

_____

51–52. While my grandparents are staying with us I am sharing, my sister's bedroom.

_____

53–54. If it keeps raining like this our, road might flood.

_____

55–56. When we got to the station his train was just pulling, in to the platform.

_____

57–58. My brother, who is always getting into trouble left his homework, at home.

_____ /12

Write an alternative viewpoint for each of these statements.

59. Recycling is a problem because you need lots of space at home for all of the different bins.

_____

60. You should spend your pocket money as soon as you get it because it is there for you to enjoy.

_____

61. Snowy days are difficult because snow is cold and slippery.

_____ /3

Draw lines to match up these punctuation marks with the correct statement.

62. Commas   are always used in pairs.

63. Speech marks   can be used to join two **clauses** that could both stand alone as sentences.

64. Semi-colons   can be used to separate a dependent and independent clause in a **complex sentence**. /3

These sentences contain **active verbs**.
Write them again, using **passive verbs**.

65. A knock at the door surprised them.

_____

66. A strong breeze rattled the windows.

_____

67. The shopkeeper counted out my change.

_____

68. A little dog chased a ball across the park.

_____

69. The postman delivered a parcel.

_____

70. A fireman rescued the kitten from the tree.

_____ /6

/70

PAPER 6

Poem 1

There once was a sailor so hairy
That his beard and moustache were quite scary
Strange mythical creatures
Roamed deep in his features
Which made his poor barber quite wary!

Poem 2

There once was a girl named Louise
With silky long hair on her knees
Her eccentric GP
Said that, "If you ask me
You need to be treated for fleas!"

Answer booklet: More English age 10–11

PAPER 1

1. once a year
2. in a village
3. He kept saying how fast he was.
4. boasting
5. He was very fast.
6. solved
7. Sam really wanted to find the treasure before Billy.
8. at the school
9. rainy
10. a tree branch
11. The rain dislodged it.
12. Billy finds the clue, then the river bank collapses.
13–14. scrabbling, grabbed
15. bloated
16. The water was deep and flowing fast.
17. Answers might include: Sam is not really concerned about Billy because he is only interested in getting the clue.
18. Answers might include: because he needed Sam to go and get help
19. mocked
20. Answers might include: No, I do not think that Sam went to get help because I think he is more interested in winning the race.
21. litter
22. climb the fallen tree to the top of the bank
23. because it has his school logo on it
24. He thinks it must have been hidden under the tree the night before, and washed down with the bank when it collapsed.
25. Answers might include: Yes, it is fair because he could run faster than the other children/because he was very brave when the bank collapsed/because Sam cheated.
26. The cat squeezed <u>between</u> the fence posts.
27. We went <u>to</u> the station and caught the train.
28. Dad made a cheese sandwich <u>for</u> me.
29. We heard a noise <u>behind</u> the door.
30. <u>Inside</u> the box was a beautiful ring.
31. A sign <u>over</u> the door said 'Closed'.
32–39. Sentences 33, 34, 38 and 39 contain active verbs.
40. If it is sunny, I will put on sunscreen.
41. If you are not careful, you could fall.
42. If I had more time, I would read the whole book.
43. If she had been earlier, she would have caught the bus.
44. If Dad was here, he would be angry.
45. If we win the match, we will win the trophy.
46–47. We could still see the ball, even though it was late, so we played another game.
48–49. At the cinema, Mum said we could have popcorn, drinks and ice-cream!
50–51. We ran down the path, jumping over the rocks, to the beach.
52–53. It was a beautiful day when, giggling happily, the girls ran out to play.
54–60. Answers will vary but each main clause must make sense on its own and the sentence should end in a full stop.
61. In the <u>meadow</u>, a flock of sheep were grazing.
62. The bride wore a <u>beautiful</u> white dress.
63. While we were <u>watching</u> the football match, it began to rain.
64. The scientist was working on a new chemical <u>formula</u>.
65. I <u>meant</u> to bring my book home but I forgot.
66. The <u>realistic</u> special effects in the film were amazing.
67. The teacher gave Mark top marks for his <u>excellent</u> story.
68. Mum said, "You need to tidy your bedrooms."
69. "You will have a test tomorrow," explained Miss Miles.
70. "I'm hungry and tired!" grumbled Ben.

PAPER 2

1–2. Answers might include: because it reuses a plastic bottle; because it provides food for wild birds
3. Answers might include: because a craft knife is very sharp and children could cut themselves
4. Answers might include: because using a clean bottle will help to keep the birdseed fresh
5. robust
6. for drawing the crosses on the bottle
7–8. pierce, punch or cut
9. The neck of a bottle is the area towards the top where the bottle narrows.
10. push string through the holes
11. limited
12. Answers might include: berries, insects
13. Answers might include: Berries appear on plants in late summer and autumn but are gone by winter. Cold winter weather kills many insects.
14. Think about the safety of birds when positioning the birdfeeder.
15. an animal that eats another animal
16. Answers might include: because a cat could walk along the wall or fence and catch the birds as they are feeding
17. It is eaten by birds.
18–19. Answers might include: bend, thread
20–22. Bullet points are used to list the things you will need for the project.
Numbered points are used to list what you need to do, in order.
The text box is used to highlight important extra information.
23. Birds perch on the twig and eat the birdseed from the V-shaped openings cut in the bottle.
24. 3m
25. Answers might include: I do think that making a birdfeeder is a good way to help wild birds because it provides them with food in the winter, when alternative sources of food are scarce.
26–27. I <u>could</u> not decide <u>which</u> shoes to buy.
28–29. Eating <u>fruit</u> and vegetables is <u>healthy</u> for you.
30–31. A warty <u>toad</u> <u>leapt</u> into the water.
32–33. Dad <u>carried</u> my little brother on his <u>shoulders</u>.

Answers to 34–38 might include:

34. I ride a pony at weekends.
35. The girls ran for the bus but they missed it.
36. Although it was raining, Jack and Tim finished their game.
37. My dogs love to play with their toys.
38. I was so full, I could not eat anything else.

Answers to 39–43 might include:

39. The cat squeezed through the gap in the fence.
40. I eventually found my phone under my bed.
41. The man behind us in the queue was rude and impatient.
42. Dad hung the picture above the fireplace.
43. Kate baked a cake for her brother's birthday party.
44. "Hurry up!" Mum shouted down the stairs.
45. "I'll see you later," said Jill as she left the house.
46. "Don't forget to do your homework," reminded Miss Smith.
47. Josh asked, "Do I have time to make a snack?"
48. "It looks as if it could rain," observed Joe.
49. "Remember your lunch money," said Dad.
50. Tara giggled, "That tickles!"

Answers to 51–52 might include:

51. We will write to winners within eight working days of the end of the competition.
52. Customer can only have a refund if they have a proper receipt.

Answers to 53–57 might include:

53. If I won the competition, I would share the prize with you.
54. If it had been sunny yesterday, we would have gone to the beach.
55. If you eat too much chocolate, you will feel sick.
56. I shall be annoyed if the train is late.
57. Mum will be furious if we break the lamp.
58. Anna finished reading her book, <u>although she was very tired</u>.
59. <u>Realising we were lost</u>, we stopped the car and asked for directions.
60. <u>When the alarm bell rang</u>, the children lined up in the playground.

61. Mum left the house, <u>locking the door behind her</u>.
62. <u>Unless I tidy my bedroom</u>, I cannot go to the cinema.
63–64. Grinning greedily, Bella piled cakes, biscuits and sweets onto her plate.
65–66. Several ducks, which were disturbed by our boat, quacked angrily as we glided by.
67–68. The bus, which was overcrowded, sped past without stopping.
69–70. Sam, Patrick and Ali settled down to watch the film, munching on their popcorn.

PAPER 3

1. overcrowding
2. being overweight
3. February
4. calling for
5–6. stride, march or striding
7–8. Answers might include: The roads are much busier than they used to be and many parents feel it is not safe for children to walk to school. More parents go out to work now and may not have time to walk to school with their children.
9–10. helps to prevent heart disease and stroke
11–13. Answers might include:

environmental benefit	less pollution
economic benefit	smaller petrol bills
social benefit	you can spend time talking to your friends

14. Answers might include: I find the environmental benefit most persuasive because I care about the environment and I worry about the pollution that comes from cars.
15–16. Answers might include: because children arrive wide awake and ready to learn; because the roads outside schools are safer if more people walk
17. reduces the speed of the traffic
18–19. posters, fliers
20. a small publicity leaflet
21. "Stride" and "ride" rhyme, so they stand out and readers are more likely to remember them.

22. The word "March" has two meanings. It can mean to walk in a determined way. It is also the name of the month in the year in which the promotion takes place. This kind of word-play stands out and makes it more memorable.

Answers to 23–25 might include:

23. Walking can help to protect you from obesity, heart disease and stroke.
24. Walking to school is the perfect way to become more active.
25. to make it seem as if they really understand what the reader might be thinking; to overcome objections they think the reader might have to walking to school
26. stranger
27. concert
28. obvious
29. concrete
30. deeper
31. village
32. pension
33. My aunt wrote the letter.
34. A big dog chased Billy.
35. A local builder built our house.
36. Wasps ruined their picnic.
37. Eve painted the best picture.
38. An experienced pilot flew the plane.
39. My music teacher tuned my guitar.

Answers to 40–49 might include:

40. Although Beth had a sore knee, she still won the race.
41. We waited at school until Mum arrived to collect us.
42. You will be cold unless you wear a coat.
43. Our teacher will be pleased if we do well in our test.
44. I like football but I don't like cricket.
45. The smoke alarm went off when I burnt my toast.
46. Mum wrapped the present carefully, then she hid it in the cupboard.
47–49. The pretty butterfly landed on a blue flower. Its wings shone in the bright sunshine. A bird sang from the branches of a nearby tree.
50. Freddie is learning to play the drums; I feel sorry for his neighbours.
51. Claire is my best friend; she can always make me smile.
52. Learning to swim is very important; it could save your life one day.

53. My dog is really naughty; she never does what she is told.
54. Ask me tomorrow; I will give you my answer then.
55. She was very careful; she did not make a single mistake.
56. I have pen-pals in Sydney, Australia; Tokyo, Japan and Paris, France.

Answers to 57–62 might include:
57. Until the show starts, we will have to wait quietly.
58. Although I am not very good at it, I love tap dancing.
59. When it stopped raining, the children ran off to play.
60. If we tidy up quickly, we will not miss any of our favourite programme.
61. My brother stormed off to his room, because he was angry.
62. We had just finished laying out our huge picnic, when the tide came in.
63–65. Although Tom's party was fantastic, I was so tired afterwards!
66–67. My uncle, who lives in Switzerland, sent me Swiss chocolates for my birthday.
68–70. My diary, games and mobile phone, which are my favourite things, were packed away carefully.

PAPER 4
1. 8am
2. because it takes quite a long time to get to the theme park
3. She was excited about the school trip.
4. mocking
5. furious
6. The coach driver wouldn't go back for the purse.
7. keepsake
8. Answers might include: No, because going back for the purse would have meant that the whole class would have less time at the theme park and that would not have been fair.
9–10. a queue of traffic, a queue for a theme park ride
11. because she did not want Charlotte to know that she was really too afraid to go on the rides
12–13. scared, nervous
14. A log flume must be a water ride, because both the writer and Ben get wet as a result of going on the ride.

15. Answers might include: Waiting for the ride was scarier than going on it because they had to wait and watch the ride go round, wondering what it was going to be like. The ride itself was over so quickly that they did not have time to think about how frightened they were.
16–18. Answers might include: once, finally, at last
19. It is likely to have taken place in the summer time, because the writer says she thinks Ben must be hot wearing both pyjamas and clothes and later she mentions that their clothes dry quickly in the sun.
20–21. PJs, jim-jams
22. Answers might include: because this is a diary entry intended only for her and her close friends to read, so formal language is unnecessary
23. Answers might include: because it encourages readers to put themselves in Ben's position and imagine how he must have felt
24. Answers might include: because they want to be able to remember what they did and how they felt on a particular day
25. Answers might include: Dear Diary … you won't believe the dreadful day I've had today!
26. leisure
27. cereal
28. granite
29. shepherd
30. tortoise
31. fossil
32. occasion

Answers to 33–40 might include:
33–34. The bus arrived, eventually, and we all piled on.
35–36. Unless you do your homework, you will get into trouble.
37–38. Cackling creepily, the witch stirred the cauldron.
39–40. Served at room temperature, strawberries are delicious.

Answers to 41–48 might include:
41. The boys clambered over the wall and disappeared.
42. A flock of birds darted across the sky.
43. Turning haughtily on her heel, she stormed out of the room.
44. With a flourish, the artist swept his brush across the canvas.

45. Enjoying the warm morning sunshine, Abbie ambled slowly to school.
46. Kate admired her reflection in the mirror.
47. Knife flashing, the chef quickly chopped the vegetables.
48. Excited, she tore at the colourful wrapping paper on the gift.
49. Counting on her fingers, Amy solved the tricky maths problem.
50. Leaving a trail of muddy paw-prints behind him, Prince headed for the sofa.
51. Although she was late, Kate did not hurry.
52. Peering through the fog, we made our way home.
53. Whenever Gran comes to stay, she always brings us presents.
54. Licking its lips, the cat watched the goldfish glide around its tank.
55. Andy ran down the path and out into the street, leaving the gate wide open.

Answers to 56–61 might include:
56. With extra training I will beat my record.
57. It always snows during January.
58. To be sure that I get to school on time, I shall leave home by 8.30.
59. Look at the chocolate around his mouth; he must have eaten the cake.
60. The most expensive phone should be the best.
61. Dad always gets home from work before 6pm.

Answers to 62–64 might include:
62. Yellow daffodils danced among the fresh spring grass.
63. Shadows crept across the dusty floor of the cave.
64. A cool breeze blew crossly through the branches of the trees.
65. Mark took another biscuit, <u>although</u> Mum had said no.
66. <u>After</u> we had finished washing the car, it started to rain.
67. Greg chose pizza, <u>but</u> I chose pasta.
68. We finished the snowman, <u>despite</u> the cold.
69. <u>In addition to</u> painting the walls of my room, we have ordered new carpets.

70. We will not miss any of the film <u>as long as</u> the bus comes soon.

PAPER 5
1. a fable
2. arrogant
3. a fruit
4. displayed
5. dashed
6. Even the smallest among us has something to offer.
7–8. stormed, growled or roared
9–10. small enough to fit in his paw; no bigger than a pomegranate
11. Answers might include: because he is angry and wants Monkey to see how dangerous he could be
12. Answers might include: because he likes the idea that he has frightened Monkey
13. Answers might be: because he is lost, so he does not realise he is walking in circles
14–15. shorter, more lost, grumpier or bigger
16–17. biggest, tallest or best
18. Answers might include: Bear is usually grumpy. We know that because the text says that he was "even grumpier than usual" after his night in the forest, meaning that he must usually be grumpy.
19. Answers might include: Bear thinks that because Monkey is so much smaller than he is. Monkey would not be able to help him.
20. He says that he could tear down the tallest tree in the forest.

Answers to 21–25 might include:
21. Monkey talks about flying to the moon because it would be impossible for him to fly to the moon, in the same way that it would be impossible to tear down the tree.
22. I do not think that Bear deserves Monkey's help because he is very rude to Monkey and threatens him.
23. because Monkey realises that Bear will have to accept his help after all
24. because repetition draws attention to the fact that Monkey keeps wanting to help Bear, and this makes Bear seem even sillier for not letting Monkey help him sooner
25. This tells me that Bear is sorry that he did not take Monkey's offer of help seriously and that now he respects him enough to show him good manners.

26. treaties
27. children
28. oxen
29. cacti
30. aircraft
31. tomatoes
32. varnishes

Answers to 33–46 might include:
33. Silently, the cat stalked the blackbird.
34. Gently, Dad picked up my sleepy baby sister.
35. Suddenly, the door flew open and a strange woman walked in.
36. Unfortunately, the shop did not have the shoes I wanted in my size.
37. Finally, the journey was over and we arrived.
38. Luckily, I had just enough money for the bus fare home.
39. Hungrily, he eyed the cakes in the shop window.
40. Despite the weight of her suitcase, Maria hurried along the platform.
41. Our team won the quiz as a result of lots of hard work.
42. I had planned to go swimming but I decided that tennis would be more fun.
43. Whenever I take my dog for a walk, she always comes back filthy.
44. As I was already late, I decided there was no point in hurrying.
45. He knew he was in trouble when he saw the head teacher approaching.
46. While I was shopping in town, I bumped into my friend Kate.
47–48. Although she was annoyed, Mum could still see the funny side.
49–50. I ordered an ice-cream, despite feeling really full.
51–52. While my grandparents are staying with us, I am sharing my sister's bedroom.
53–54. If it keeps raining like this, our road might flood.
55–56. When we got to the station, his train was just pulling in to the platform.
57–58. My brother, who is always getting into trouble, left his homework at home.

Answers to 59–61 might include:
59. Recycling is easy because there are lots of recycling centres to take your recyclable rubbish to.

60. You should save your pocket money until you have enough to buy something you really want.
61. Snowy days are wonderful because you can build a snowman or have a snowball fight.
62. Commas can be used to separate a dependent and independent clause in a complex sentence.
63. Speech marks are always used in pairs.
64. Semi-colons can be used to join two clauses that could both stand alone as sentences.
65. They were surprised by a knock at the door.
66. The windows were rattled by a strong breeze.
67. My change was counted out by the shopkeeper.
68. The ball was chased across the park by a little dog.
69. A parcel was delivered by the postman.
70. The kitten was rescued from the tree by a fireman.

PAPER 6
1. wandered through
2. imaginary
3. someone who cuts men's hair
4. cautious

Answers to 5–15 might include:
5. You wouldn't expect mythical creatures to be in someone's beard.
6. The beard and moustache must be very big!
7–8. The best line is: "They even included a fairy." This is because fairy rhymes with hairy and scary, and fairies, like mythical creatures, are imaginary.
9. A General Practitioner, or family doctor
10. Silky long hair is usually considered an attractive feature, but it does not usually grow on girls' knees!
11. because she is worried about having long hair on her knees
12. You might expect the doctor to explain to Louise why she has grown hair on her knees and how it could be treated. Instead, what he says sounds more like something a vet might say about a pet!
13. toes, nose (to rhyme with Rose)

14–15. The best line is, "You should shave before anyone sees." This is because sees rhymes with Louise and knees and it maintains the rhythm of the poem.

16. limerick

17. amused (Limericks are intended to entertain.)

Answers to 18–23 might include:

18–19. Some things are believable but there are also things that are not. For example, some men are very hairy, and people do go to their doctor if they have a health problem. However, people do not really have mythical creatures in their hair, or long hair on their knees.

20. I do not feel sorry for the people in these poems because they are not real, and the things that happen to them would not happen to a real person.

21–23. Both poems have five lines; lines one, two and five of both poems rhyme; the first lines of both poems are similar (one starts "There was a" and the other starts "There once was a".

24. making fun of a fictional character

25. Answers will vary, but should include reasons to back them up.

26. orchestra

27. graceful

28. pollution

29. peaceful

30. television

31. independent

32. separate

Answers to 33–38 might include:

33–34. Rose's are red, but Claire prefers blue shoes.
At first, the sentence seems to be describing the colour of roses, the flower. Adding an apostrophe to "Roses" makes it clear that the sentence is about not just Claire's shoes, but about someone called Rose's shoes, too.

35–36. When it was time to eat, she went into the garden and called her friends' names.
At first, the sentence seems to be saying that the girl went into the garden and said unkind things to her friends. Adding an apostrophe makes it clear that

in fact she called out to them, using their names.

37–38. Our spoilt dog knows it's master.
At first, the sentence seems to say that the dog recognises who its master is. Adding an apostrophe makes it clear that the spoilt dog knows that *it* is master!

39–46.

Time connectives	after	finally
Comparing connectives	similarly	like
Cause and effect connectives	because	so
Illustrating connectives	for example	such as

47. My project will be finished by Thursday.

48. During the summer, the beach gets crowded.

49. At bedtime, they got home.

50. We bought a gold necklace for Gemma.

51. From the museum, we walked home.

52. They found a spiral staircase inside the castle.

53–55. Punctuation, as you know, will help you to understand a sentence's meaning.

56–57. Crossing her fingers for luck, Imogen rolled the small, red dice.

58–59. Daniel, Matthew and David rushed into the house, leaving muddy footprints behind them.

60–61. "What on earth have you been up to?" fussed Mum, looking at our filthy clothes.

Answers to 62–64 might include:

62. the sinking sun stains the sky

63. the tides turn tirelessly

64. a tidily trimmed treat

65. If Henry VIII had not had so many wives, he might not have been so well known.

66. If I am ten years old, after my next birthday I will be eleven.

67. Modern medicines could have prevented many of the horrible illnesses people used to suffer from, if they had been invented then.

68. Mum says I can stay up late tomorrow night if I go to bed early tonight.

69. If our car had not broken down on the way to the theatre, we would have seen the show.

70. We must make sure we water our vegetable plants if it does not rain soon.

PAPER 7

1. cot

2. sailing boat

3. sea

4. jetty

5. leaning

6. because she wanted her parents to hear how angry she was

7. to give her a chance to calm down

8. Answers might include: I think Lucy is most angry with herself, because she knows that if she had not lost her temper, she would have been allowed to go to the park.

9. because the text says that her temper had let her down "again", which shows it must have happened before

10. Answers might include: It is possible that Lucy has climbed down from her window before, so she knows how to do it.

11. Answers might include: I do think leaving the house was irresponsible, because if something happened to Lucy, nobody would know where to look for her.

12. to enjoy the view of the sun on the sea

13–14. The sun was shining in her eyes. The yacht was a long way away.

15. She was going to spend it on sweets.

16. She had left it charging at home.

17. Answers might include: She does not want to waste the coastguard's time if there is nothing wrong/in case another boat really is in trouble somewhere else.

18. No, because the text says there is nobody else around who could have seen the yacht.

19. It could sink.

20. vessel

Answers to 21–25 might include:

21. I do not think Lucy really had a choice, because it is far more important to keep the crew of the yacht safe than to stay out of trouble.

22. I do not think Lucy's decision makes up for being dishonest but in the end the crew of the yacht was lucky that she was brave enough to face her parents.
23. I do think Lucy's parents will be angry with her for sneaking out but they will be proud too, because she made the right decision in the end.
24. The title is 'Yacht rescue!', so I think the coastguard will rescue the crew and tow the yacht back to the shore.
25. I think the writer does this because it encourages the reader to think about what is happening from Lucy's point of view.
26. receipt
27. restaurant
28. hospitality
29. category
30. discipline
31. maintenance
32. relevant
33. Babies <u>cry</u> when they are hungry.
34. The boys <u>did</u> a good job tidying their rooms.
35. The little boy cried when he <u>dropped</u> his ice-cream.
36. In summer there <u>is</u> usually quite a bit of sunshine.
37. The girls <u>were</u> ready for their dancing lesson.
38. Our team <u>won</u> the tournament.
39. I <u>wish</u> it would stop raining.
40. instructions
41. recount
42. advert
43. discussion text
44. fairy tale
45. explanatory text

Answers to 46–59 might include:
46–47. "Your car just needs petrol," explained the mechanic.
48–49. "My new shoes are uncomfortable," complained Kate.
50–51. "Remember to leave the cloakroom tidy," said Mr Hoskins.
52–53. "I wonder what time it is," said John.
54–55. "That test was difficult," grumbled Jenny.
56–57. "Your dog will be fine," said the vet.
58–59. "There will be sunshine tomorrow," promised the weatherman.

60. sprinted
61. devoured
62. strode
63. stared
64. sliced
65. asked
66. gasped
67. giggled

Answers to 68–70 might include:
68. Huge waves crashed onto the beach, before roaring back out to sea.
69. The car came to a screeching halt, its horn wailing.
70. The water gurgled as it spiralled down the plughole.

PAPER 8
1. chopped down
2. persuaded
3. lions
4. fairy tale
5. spring
6. to cut into logs to sell
7–8. Answers might include: He has barely enough food for himself. He ignores the hunger in his belly.
9. He counts them as friends because he lives alone.
10. because he sees one fly into the tree carrying a twig and birds often use twigs to make their nests
11. because he is running out of time to find a tree, cut it down and chop it into logs before the sun sets

Answers to 12–22 might include:
12–13. entranced, enchanted
14. No, because he is confused and afraid when he comes across the talking tree.
15–16. because their nest is safe; because their friend the wood-cutter has freed the woman from the tree
17. Once the woman is freed from the tree, she magically transports it to the wood-cutter's wood store.
18. The woman by the stove is the woman who was trapped in the tree by the witch.
19. We know this because her dress is described using the same words used to describe the tree.
20. I do think the wood-cutter's kindness is rewarded in the story because he meets and falls in love with the woman he rescues from the tree, so he is not lonely any more.

21–22. once upon a time, happily ever after
23–25. Answers will vary.
26. fascination
27. fashion
28. electrician
29. mission or million
30. mansion
31. Egyptian
32. pressure
33. The nest in the hedge was built by a bird.
34. Our sand castle was washed away by the tide.
35. The blossom was blown off the trees by the wind.
36. The letter was posted by Kate.
37. We were slowed down on the way home by heavy traffic.
38. My shoe was chewed by my dog.
39. Puddles were left in the street by heavy rain.
40. Long shadows were cast across the lawn by the setting sun.
41–43. Despite her being terribly nervous, Claire's ballet exam went very well.
44–46. A large cake, dripping with chocolate icing, sat in the shop window.
47–49. "Stop!" shouted Rory, Max and Jonathon, running after the bus.

Answers to 50–55 might include:
50. I must have dropped my purse when I was getting off the bus.
51. Although the sun was shining, the wind was chilly.
52. Milly was excited because it was her birthday.
53. Despite the rain, we all enjoyed our school trip.
54. After feeding our rabbit, we cleaned out its hutch.
55. I finished my homework and packed my schoolbag.
56. If you had arrived earlier, you <u>would</u> have seen the whole film.
57. "If you are not careful, you <u>might</u> fall," warned Mum.
58. If Mum has to work late tonight, she <u>might</u> be too tired to go out.
59. You <u>should</u> always say please when you ask for something.
60. We <u>will</u> get wet if it rains.
61. When you have finished your drink you <u>should</u> recycle the bottle.
62. true
63. false

64. true
65–70. Residents in Ⓒastle Street were left puzzled on Thursday, after discovering the road covered in building⌢ blocks, marbles and jigsaw pieces. The mystery was solved later in the day, when local toy company Terrific Ⓣoys revealed that the doors of one of itⓈs delivery trucks had opened by mistake, spilling⌢ toys into the road⌢.

PAPER 9

1. There are almost as many pet dogs in the UK as there are children under 16.
2. threat
3. ugly
4. most
5. newspapers
6. Answers might include: I am surprised about how many dogs there are in the UK because I would expect to see more dogs out walking.
7–8. dog mess; aggressive dogs
9. young children
10. to keep dogs out, so there will be no dog mess
11–12. dealing with stray dogs; enforcing laws about picking up dog mess
13–14. Answers might include: people running; sports teams
15. Answers might include: because they might not have time to walk their own dog; because they might not be able to walk very far
16–17. Health risk: toxocariasis. Health benefit: dog walking is good exercise

Answers to 18–22 might include:

18–20. employing dog wardens; fencing play areas; providing special bins for dog mess
21. I do think that banning dogs from parks would reduce the amount of dog mess in parks, but people would walk their dogs in the street instead, so you might get more mess there.
22. I do not think dogs should be banned from public parks because most dog owners do take responsibility for their pets.
23–24. on the other hand; however
25. Answers might include: I do agree that the UK is a nation of animal

lovers because so many dogs are kept as pets.

26. floor
27. shake
28. plate
29. lose
30. rare
31. grow
32. roll
33. she
34. they/we/he/she
35. he
36. they
37. it/she/he
38. we
39–40. The table was laden with delicious foods: cakes, pastries and tiny sandwiches.
41–43. We saw lots of different animals at the zoo: lions, elephants, penguins and a baby giraffe.
44–45. I have my favourite lessons today: English, maths and art.
46. Rob <u>carefully</u> painted his model.
47. The tide <u>gradually</u> crept up the beach.
48. The tree lent <u>dangerously</u> over the path.
49. Nina drew her graph <u>accurately</u>.
50. The young children clapped <u>excitedly</u> when the magician appeared.
51. Our cat jumped down <u>lightly</u> from the garden wall.
52. <u>Noisily</u>, the class clattered down the steps and into the playground.

Answers to 53–55 might include:

53. A rhyming dictionary is a book that lists words alphabetically and suggests words that rhyme with each one. They can be useful when you are writing rhyming poetry.
54. An encyclopaedia is a book that lists general knowledge topics in alphabetical order and provides information about them. They can be useful when you are producing a project for school.
55. A thesaurus is a book that lists words alphabetically and lists words with a similar meaning. They can be useful in story writing to find interesting descriptive words.
56–57. "I like this one," said Sophie, holding up a blue dress.
58–59. "Let's go to the beach today," suggested Dad.

60–63. "I know you're busy," ventured Mark, "but could you drive me to the shops?"

Answers to 64–70 might include:

64. "This soup is cold," complained the man, gruffly.
65. "There's a spider!" shrieked Grace, leaping onto a chair.
66. "That's really funny!" giggled Anna.
67. Dad asked, "Have you seen my keys?"
68. "Get out of my room," snapped Greg, crossly.
69. "That's a pretty top," remarked Gran.
70. Jack grumbled, "It's not fair!"

PAPER 10

1. scornfully
2. ramshackle
3. annoying
4. They have fallen through the floor of an old house they were exploring.
5. because the place they have fallen into has no natural light and the children cannot find their torch
6. She blames Mark.
7. Answers might include: I do not think it is fair because even if it was Mark's idea to explore the house, the others could have chosen not to go with him.
8. Answers might include: I do not think she really means it, because the stage directions use the word "sarcastically", which means saying things that you do not really mean.
9–10. "you ask if we're OK!", "Glad to help!"; or "Oh, well done you two!"

Answers to 11–18 might include:

11. because thinking about spiders might frighten her, so Tom changes the subject
12. I think Tom behaves most calmly because he does not argue with the others and thinks about finding the torch and looking for a way out.
13. I think there was someone else already in the room when the children fell and Zoe grabs their foot.
14. because she discovers that it isn't Tom or Mark's foot, as she thought
15. because people tend to speak more quickly when they are nervous or afraid

16. I think the person who was already in the room walks across the floor.
17. I think the door leads into a secret tunnel under the house.
18. I think that Zoe and Mark will argue about whether to go through the door, but in the end they will because there is no other way out.
19. stage directions
20. They tell the actors and director what characters need to do or how they should speak.
21–23. shuffling sounds as the children look for the torch; the clicking sound of the torch switch; dragging footsteps across the stage
24. Because the stage is in darkness, we cannot see the characters faces, or how they move, so we rely on tone of voice to understand how the characters are feeling.
25. Answers might include: I think facial expressions are more important than dialogue right at the end of the act, when the door opens and the stage becomes dimly lit, when we see the children for the first time.
26. furius (furious)
27. favourate (favourite)
28. posess (possess)
29. wierd (weird)
30. appeer (appear)

31. suceed (succeed)
32. forteen (fourteen)
33. My little sister is terribly disorganised.
34. A rare butterfly fluttered through the garden.
35. I did not play football because I had a sore knee.
36. The scary film was totally terrifying.
37. "You're such a lucky girl!" said Mum, paying for the shoes.
38. Dad was furious when we broke the antique vase.
39. The azure sea glistened brightly in the sunshine.
40–41. I put ham, lettuce, cucumber and tomato in my sandwich.
42–43. Although it's bad for you if you eat too much, I do love ice-cream!
44–45. "Your room is a disgrace," complained Mum.
46–48. "Why are you late?" asked Mrs Bridges, looking at the clock.
Answers to 49–51 might include:
49. as white as icing sugar
50. as old as the pyramids
51. as big as a mountain
Answers to 52–58 might include:
52. The woman carried a large green bag.
53. I took the books back to the library.

54. They walked carefully across the road.
55. I crept quietly down the stairs.
56. The door was propped open with a thick, heavy book.
57. Chess is a difficult game to play.
58. The children played in the sea.
Answers to 59–64 might include:
59–60. Commas can be used to separate clauses in a complex sentence.
Although she was scared of the dark, she went into the creepy house.
61–62. Semi-colons can be used instead of a connective to join two clauses that could stand on their own as complete sentences.
Simon was hungry; he ordered a large pizza.
63–64. Apostrophes can be used to show that something belongs to someone/where letters are missing from a word.
We played with Kate's puppy/I'll show you the way.
65. river
66. badly
67. very
68. blew
69. cruel
70. the

Questions 1–8 are about Poem 1.

Underline your answers.

1. Which of these words or **phrases** is most similar in meaning to "roamed"?

   raced through   wandered through   slid through   patrolled

2. Which of these words or phrases is most similar in meaning to "mythical"?

   microscope   monstrous   imaginary   extinct

3. What is a barber?

   a friend   someone who captures mythical creatures

   someone who cuts men's hair   a hairy sailor

4. Which of these words is most similar in meaning to the word "wary"?

   weird   brave   ill   cautious   /4

Answer these questions.

5. Why might the sailor's barber feel wary?

   _____

6. What is humorous about the idea of mythical creatures roaming in the sailor's beard and moustache?

   _____

7–8. Which of these would be a good alternative to the final line? Tick your answer and give a reason for your choice.

   He decided to live in a dairy.   He decided to have a shave.

   They even included a fairy.   They were even home to a unicorn.

   _____   /4

Questions 9–15 are about Poem 2.

Answer these questions.

9. What is a GP?

_____

10. What is humorous about the idea of a girl with silky long hair on her knees?

_____

11. Why might Louise go to see her GP?

_____

12. What is surprising about what the doctor says to Louise?

_____

13. If the girl in the poem was called Rose, think of a part of her that could be hairy instead of her knees. Give a reason for your choice.

_____

14–15. Which of these would be a good alternative to the final line? Tick your answer and give a reason for your choice.

I need a holiday.   You should shave before anyone sees.

You should shampoo these knees.   There is nothing wrong with you.

_____   /7

Questions 16–25 are about both poems.

Answer these questions.

16. What is the special name for this type of poem? Underline your answer.

haiku   sonnet   kenning   limerick

17. How do you think the writer wants you to feel when you read these poems?

_____

18–19. Which statement best describes the content of these poems? Tick your answer and give a reason for your choice.

Everything in them is completely believable.

Nothing in them is at all believable.

Some things are believable but there are also things that are not.

The texts have a strong moral message.

_____

_____

20. Do you feel sorry for the people in these poems? Give a reason for your answer.

_____

_____

21–23. Write down three things you notice about the structure of both poems.

_____

_____

_____

24. What purpose do you think this type of poem is most suited to? Tick your answer.

telling someone you love them

making fun of a fictional character

describing a beautiful natural feature

telling a long, detailed story

25. Do you enjoy this kind of poem? Give a reason for your answer, including what you do, or do not, like.

_____

/10

Write down the correct spelling for these words.

26. orchistra _____

27. graseful _____

28. polution _____

29. pieceful _____

30. telivision _____

31. independant _____

32. seperate _____

/7

Change the **punctuation** in these **sentences** to alter the meaning. Then describe how the meaning has changed.

33–34. Roses are red, but Claire prefers blue shoes.

_____

_____

35–36. When it was time to eat, she went into the garden and called her friends names.

_____

_____

37–38. Our spoilt dog knows its master.

_____

_____

/6

Sort the **connective** words and phrases into the correct sections of the chart.

39–46. for example, after, such as, because, similarly, so, like, finally

Time connectives		
Comparing connectives		
Cause and effect connectives		
Illustrating connectives		

/8

Write each sentence again, placing the phrase in *italics* somewhere else in the sentence.

47. *By Thursday*, my project will be finished.

_____

48. The beach gets crowded *during the summer*.

_____

49. They got home *at bedtime*.

_____

50. *For Gemma*, we bought a gold necklace.

_____

51. We walked home *from the museum*.

_____

52. *Inside the castle*, they found a spiral staircase.

_____   /6

Add correct punctuation to these sentences.

53–55. Punctuation as you know will help you to understand a sentences meaning.

56–57. Crossing her fingers for luck Imogen rolled the small red dice.

58–59. Daniel Matthew and David rushed into the house leaving muddy footprints behind them.

60–61. "What on earth have you been up to? fussed Mum looking at our filthy clothes.   /9

Using **alliteration**, write a phrase of at least three words to describe these things.

62. a sunset

_____

63. the sea

_____

64. a birthday present

_____ /3

Choose the best word from the brackets to complete each sentence.

65. If Henry VIII had not had so many wives, he _____ not have been so well known. (could, might, must)

66. If I am ten years old, after my next birthday I _____ be eleven. (will, was, can)

67. Modern medicines _____ have prevented many of the horrible illnesses people used to suffer from, if they had been invented then. (should, must, could)

68. Mum says I _____ stay up late tomorrow night if I go to bed early tonight. (would, can, then)

69. If our car had not broken down on the way to the theatre, we _____ have seen the show. (can, will, would)

70. We _____ make sure we water our vegetable plants if it does not rain soon. (can, must, could)

/6

/70

Yacht rescue!

Lucy banged her bedroom door shut, a little harder than was strictly necessary, and flopped down on her bed. It wasn't fair! They just didn't understand her. Making sure they could hear her anger from downstairs, she kicked the headboard of her bed then sat up, sulkily.

It had been raining for weeks and this was the first really warm, dry evening of spring.   5
Everyone had planned to meet in the park this evening. Most of them would be there already but where was she? Stuck at home, that's where. The worst of it was that Lucy knew she really only had herself to blame. Mum had said she could go, but that she had to be back by seven o'clock. Lucy had complained loudly that was too early, and before she knew what had happened, she had been sent to her room. Once again, her temper had let her down.   10

Lucy knew her parents would leave her to calm down and she probably wouldn't see them for the rest of the evening. Why keep her here if they weren't even going to spend time with her? She might as well not be here at all!

A thought began to form in Lucy's mind. Her bedroom window looked out onto the flat roof of the kitchen extension below. From there, she knew she could climb down onto the water   15
butt, and down onto the patio. They would never know she had gone!

Wasting no more time, Lucy grabbed a jacket and hunted about on her desk for some change in case she wanted to buy some sweets later. She could only find 50p but, she reasoned, that was better than nothing. She was safely on the patio and on her way to the park in a matter of moments.   20

The route to the park took Lucy along the seafront for a while and she slowed down to take in the view of the sea glistening in the late evening sunshine. Something on the horizon caught her eye and she stopped and peered into the glare, trying to make out what it was. A small yacht bobbed on the sea in the distance. Lucy was no sailor but something about the vessel just didn't look right, even from this distance. Lucy wondered what to do. She had   25
left her mobile phone charging at home, but even if she had it with her, did she really want to alert the coastguard when she wasn't really sure that anything was wrong?

There was nobody else in sight. Lucy decided it was up to her to do something, but what? Thoughtfully, she fingered the 50p in her pocket. There was a coin-operated telescope on the stone quay that tourists used in the summer to look out to sea. It would give her a better   30
view of the yacht, and then she could decide what to do for the best.

As soon as Lucy focused the telescope on the little boat she could see that it was in trouble. Its sail was hanging at an odd angle and it was listing in the water. It was probably taking on water, she thought.

Lucy knew she had to act quickly, but a fresh thought came to her. Without a mobile phone   35
she would have to find some other way of raising the alarm. The nearest building with a phone
was her own home, but as far as her parents were concerned she was safely upstairs. The
house had no view of the sea, so there could only be one way she could have seen the yacht.
If she went home to call the coastguard, Lucy knew she would be in big trouble. If she didn't,
she would be putting the crew of the stricken yacht in serious danger.   40

Lucy thought about how quickly a little boat like that could become waterlogged. She had no
choice. Glancing again at the horizon, Lucy turned and raced for home.

Underline your answers.

1. Which of these words does the word "yacht" rhyme with?

yak   matched   yolk   cot

2. Which of these words or **phrases** is closest in meaning to the word "yacht"?

pier   sailing boat   passenger ferry   canoe

3. Which of these words does the word "quay" rhyme with?

sway   sea   glue   near

4. Which of these words is closest in meaning to the word "quay"?

jetty   bollard   wall   step

5. What does "listing" mean? (line 33)

leaning   leaping   racing   sinking

6. Why did Lucy kick the headboard of her bed? Tick your answer.

because it had been raining for weeks

because it was the first warm evening of the spring

because she wanted her parents to hear how angry she was

because the bed made her angry

7. Why does Lucy think her parents will leave her alone?

because they are very angry with her   so that she can sneak out without them knowing

to give her a chance to calm down   so that she cannot go to the park

/7

Answer these questions.

8. Who do you think Lucy is most angry with: her parents, or herself for losing her temper? Give a reason for your answer.

_____

_____

9. How do we know that this is not the first time Lucy has lost her temper?

_____

_____

10. Suggest a reason why Lucy "knew" she would be able to climb from the roof onto the water butt.

_____

_____

11. Do you think that leaving the house without permission was irresponsible? Give a reason for your answer.

_____

12. Why did Lucy slow down when she was walking along the seafront?

_____

13–14. Give two reasons why Lucy could not see the yacht clearly at first.

_____

_____

15. What does Lucy originally plan to do with the 50p she used for the telescope?

_____

16. Why did Lucy not have her mobile phone with her?

_____

17. Why do you think Lucy doesn't want to alert the coastguard until she is sure something is wrong with the yacht?

_____

_____

18. Could Lucy have left it to someone else to raise the alarm? Give a reason for your answer.

_____

19. What might eventually happen to a boat that is "taking on water" (lines 33–34)?

_____

20. Find and write down another word in the text with a similar meaning to "yacht" and "boat".

_____

21. Do you think Lucy really had a choice? Give a reason for your answer.

_____

22. In the end, do you think Lucy's decision to go home and get help makes up for being dishonest in the first place? Give a reason for your answer.

_____

23. The story ends before Lucy gets home. Do you think her parents will be angry with her? Give a reason for your answer.

_____

24. What do you think happens to the crew and the yacht at the end of this story?

_____

_____

25. In several places the text includes questions (e.g. lines 7, 13, and 27). Why do you think the writer chose to do this?

_____

_____ /18

Underline the correctly spelt word in each group.

26.	receit	receipt	reciept
27.	restaurent	resturant	restaurant
28.	hospitality	hospitalitey	hospitallity
29.	categry	category	catagary
30.	discipline	disipline	disciplin
31.	maintainance	maintenence	maintenance
32.	relevent	revelent	relevant

/7

Underline the errors in these **sentences**.

33. Babies cries when they are hungry.

34. The boys done a good job tidying their rooms.

35. The little boy cried when he drop his ice-cream.

36. In summer there are usually quite a bit of sunshine.

37. The girls was ready for their dancing lesson.

38. Our team winned the tournament.

39. I wishes it would stop raining.

/7

Draw lines to join up each sentence with the type of text it is most likely to have come from.

40. First, attach part A to part B using 1 × 15mm screw.   recount

41. I was crossing the road when the black car sped past.   explanatory text

42. Try new Spider-be-gone, for all your bug-busting needs!   instructions

43. Sweets are lovely, but are too many bad for you?   fairy tale

44. Once upon a time, there lived a princess.   discussion text

45. Oxygen is carried around the body in the blood.   advert   /6

Write these sentences again, replacing the **reported speech** with **direct speech**. Include the correct **punctuation**.

46–47. The mechanic explained that our car just needed petrol.

_____

48–49. Kate complained that her new shoes were uncomfortable.

_____

50–51. Mr Hoskins reminded the class to leave the cloakroom tidy.

_____

52–53. John wondered what time it was.

_____

54–55. Jenny grumbled that the test had been difficult.

_____

56–57. The vet told us our dog was going to be fine.

_____

58–59. The weatherman promised there would be sunshine tomorrow.

_____ /14

> Underline a **verb** from each bracket to
> complete each sentence in the best way.

60. The athlete (scampered, scurried, sprinted) across the finish line.

61. Having missed breakfast, Sam (nibbled, devoured, tasted) his lunch.

62. After leaving home late, Mum (dawdled, strode, ambled) to the station.

63. Our teacher (stared, peeped, glanced) at the girls who were giggling on the back row.

64. Dad (dissected, carved, sliced) tomatoes for the salad.

65. I (begged, asked, pleaded) for a ticket to the town centre.

66. Mum (choked, panted, gasped) when she saw her birthday cake.

67. The little girl (guffawed, giggled, cackled) at the funny clown.

/8

> Write a sentence to describe each of these things, using **onomatopoeia**.

68. a storm at sea

_____

69. a car stopping suddenly

_____

70. water draining down a plughole

_____ /3

/70

PAPER 8

The lady in the tree

Once upon a time, in a far-away land, there lived a poor wood-cutter. He worked each day from sunrise to sunset, felling trees and chopping them into logs to be burnt on the fires of the rich people who lived in the nearby town.

The wood-cutter lived alone; he had barely enough food for himself, let alone a wife. All the   5
same, he was lonely and longed to share his little log cabin in the forest.

On one particularly beautiful spring morning, the wood-cutter headed far into the forest, as usual. Spring was his favourite time of year and he stopped now and again to listen to birds singing in the branches, or to admire a family of fox cubs playing in a clearing. Living alone, he counted the creatures of the woodland as his friends and shared their enjoyment of the   10
warmer weather. In particular, he took great care not to fell those trees in which he suspected birds might be nesting. He observed this habit even when doing so meant a longer trek into the forest, and never expected anything in return. Although he would not have known this, such kindness rarely goes unrewarded.

The wood-cutter had planned to cut down a particularly tall tree on this morning. Not only   15
would it provide plenty of firewood, it had been damaged by winter storms and would soon become dangerous. However, as he prepared to swing his axe on this fateful morning, the wood-cutter noticed a robin dart into the branches. A second later, it flew off again, instantly followed by the return of a second bird, carrying twigs in its beak. Just in time, the wood-cutter realised that the robins were nesting in the tree.   20

Wishing them well, the wood-cutter walked wearily on, until he came upon a tree he could not remember having seen before. Its trunk was slender and covered with bark so pale it shone like silver in the sunlight. Knowing he needed to fell a tree soon if he was to have it chopped into logs before the light failed, he once again lifted his axe.

This time it was not a bird that halted the woodman's axe, but a mysterious voice. "Please,   25
stop!" it sounded. "I am not what I seem. Put down your axe and talk a while." Confused, the wood-cutter lowered his axe and looked about him for the source of the strange voice he had heard.

"Show yourself," he replied, growing afraid.

"I am here, before you," said the voice, and at that moment the wind caught the leaves of the   30
tree, and they tinkled like tiny bells. "I have not always been as you see me now," said the voice, seeming to come from the tree itself. "I once roamed the forest as you do, in the service of a witch who lives at the far edge of the forest. One day she grew afraid that I longed to leave the forest, so she trapped me here in this tree."

The wood-cutter, who had never encountered a talking tree, listened open-mouthed. He was entranced by the voice but struggled to believe that it came from the tree before him, and remembered that unless he delivered a load of logs to the town by nightfall, he would have no money to buy food to eat.   35

As if it could read his mind, the tree continued. "I know you are tired and hungry, but you can free me. Just go home and I promise all will be well."   40

Something about the strange voice had enchanted the wood-cutter and convinced him to believe what it said. Ignoring his tired legs and the hunger in his belly, he turned and headed for home. The pair of robins fluttered ahead of him, chirruping happily.

When he reached his cabin he could scarcely believe his eyes. His wood store, which had been empty that morning, was stacked full of logs, ready to be delivered to the town. Even better, delicious cooking smells wafted out of the cabin towards him. Curious, the woodman went into his cabin. By the stove stood a beautiful woman in a dress so pale it shone like silver.   45

"Thank you for freeing me," said the woman, simply. "The witch was wrong. I never wanted to leave the forest. I just wanted to be free to choose."   50

Little by little, one day at a time, the wood-cutter and the beautiful woman grew to love each other as much as they loved the forest, and together they lived, in the little log cabin, happily ever after.

Underline your answers.

1. What does "felling" (line 3) mean?

   fallen   chopped down   damaged   silver

2. What does the word "convinced" (line 41) mean?

   forced   persuaded   worried   frightened

3. Baby foxes are called cubs (line 9). Which of these animals also have babies that are called cubs?

   rabbits   lions   monkeys   dogs

4. What kind of story is this?

   myth   dilemma story   fairy tale   adventure

5. At what time of year does the story take place?

   spring   summer   autumn   winter   /5

Answer these questions.

6. Why does the wood-cutter cut down trees? Underline your answer.

   to build a log cabin   to cut into logs to sell

   because the trees were damaged by a winter storm   because he loves the forest

7–8. Find two pieces of evidence in the text that suggest the wood-cutter does not always have enough to eat.

   _____

   _____

9. Why does the wood-cutter take special care of the animals in the forest?

   _____

10. Why does the wood-cutter think that robins are nesting in the tall tree?

_____

11. Why does the wood-cutter originally decide to cut down the silver tree?

_____

12–13. Find and write down two words that suggest the voice in the forest has some sort of magical power over the wood-cutter.

_____   _____

14. Do you think magical things often happen to the wood-cutter? Give a reason for your answer.

_____

15–16. Give two reasons why the robins were chirruping happily (line 43).

_____

_____

17. How do you think the wood-cutter's wood store came to be full when he returned home?

_____

18. Who is the woman by the stove in line 47?

_____

19. Give a reason for your answer to Question 18.

_____

20. In line 40, the text suggests that the wood-cutter's kindness is likely to be rewarded. Do you think this happens in the story, and if so, how?

_____

21–22. Find and write down two **phrases** that often appear in this type of story.

_____

_____

23–25. Write three **sentences** describing how the wood-cutter might feel at the end of the story.

_____

_____

_____ /20

Add the missing letters to correctly complete each of these words.

26. fascina_____ _____on

27. fa_____ _____ion

28. electri_____ _____an

29. mi_____ _____ion

30. man_____ _____on

31. Egypt_____ _____n

32. pre_____ _____ ure /7

These sentences use **active verbs**. Write them again, using **passive verbs**.

33. A bird built the nest in the hedge.

_____

34. The tide washed our sand castle away.

_____

35. The wind blew the blossom off the trees.

_____

36. Kate posted the letter.

_____

37. On the way home, heavy traffic slowed us down.

_____

38. My dog chewed my shoe.

_____

39. Heavy rain left puddles in the street.

_____

40. The setting sun cast long shadows across the lawn.

_____   /8

Add the missing **punctuation** to these sentences.

41–43. Despite her being terribly nervous Claires ballet exam went very well

44–46. A large cake dripping with chocolate icing sat in the shop window

47–49. Stop!" shouted Rory Max and Jonathon running after the bus.   /9

Add a suitable **connective** word or **phrase** to complete each sentence.

50. I must have dropped my purse _____ I was getting off the bus.

51. _____ the sun was shining, the wind was chilly.

52. Milly was excited _____ it was her birthday.

53. _____ the rain, we all enjoyed our school trip.

54. _____ feeding our rabbit, we cleaned out its hutch.

55. I finished my homework _____ packed my schoolbag.

/6

Underline the best word from the brackets to complete each sentence.

56. If you had arrived earlier, you (should, would, will) have seen the whole film.

57. "If you are not careful, you (should, might, can) fall," warned Mum.

58. If Mum has to work late tonight, she (might, should, can) be too tired to go out.

59. You (can, should, could) always say please when you ask for something.

60. We (can, will, should) get wet if it rains.

61. When you have finished your drink, you (should, might, cannot) recycle the bottle.

/6

Decide whether each of these statements about **paragraphs** is true or false.

62. You should start a new paragraph when you start writing about a new topic. _____

63. It is wrong to start a new paragraph just because someone new is speaking. _____

64. Starting a new paragraph can help you to create dramatic effect in your writing. _____

/3

Circle the punctuation errors in this piece of text.

65–70. Residents in castle Street were left puzzled on Thursday, after discovering the road covered in building, blocks, marbles and jigsaw pieces. The mystery was solved later in the day, when local toy company Terrific toys revealed that the doors of one of it's delivery trucks had opened by mistake, spilling, toys into the road;

/6

/70

PAPER 9

Dogs: man's best friend or public menace?
Studies show that almost a third of UK households are home to at least one dog, adding up
to as many as eight million pet dogs. Is it time to ban dogs from our public parks?

There are almost as many pet dogs in the UK as there are children under the age of 16, and
with dog-walking and children's play accounting for a high proportion of park usage, our   5
public spaces are under increasing pressure. While the majority of dog owners do take
responsibility for their dogs, most parents of young children will tell you that dog mess and
aggressive dogs are frequent problems in many public parks.

Almost everyone would agree that leaving dog mess in a public place is unacceptable. Not
only is it unsightly and smelly, it poses a real risk to human health because it spreads   10
disease. In particular, a rare but serious condition called toxocariasis which causes blindness
in humans, especially young children. Many play areas are fenced by councils to keep dogs
out, but dog mess can still be found on many of the sports pitches children use. Although
councils do employ dog wardens to deal with stray dogs and enforce laws about cleaning up
dog mess, they cannot patrol all parks all of the time. Banning all dogs from public parks   15
could dramatically reduce the dog mess being left and make wardens' jobs easier.

On the other hand, many dog owners would never dream of leaving their dog's mess in a
public place. The majority of dog owners do clean up after their pets and use the bins
provided by councils to dispose of dog mess safely. Many people argue that those dog
owners who ignore requests to clean up after their pets would also ignore a ban on taking   20
their animals into parks. If this was the case, responsible owners and their pets would be
needlessly prevented from enjoying the parks that their taxes pay for, yet dog mess would
continue to be a problem.

Dog mess is only part of the problem. There has also been a lot of coverage in the press
about dangerous dogs on Britain's streets. However, while dogs are generally kept on leads   25
by roads, owners tend to take off their dogs' leads in parks. Some people feel that many of
these dogs are not under their owners' control in public parks, and that some dogs are
simply too dangerous to be off the lead. Megan Wright visits her local park regularly with her
two young children. "We love using the park but my children are frightened by some of the
dogs running around. Some of them jump up at the children, and when their owners call   30
them back they just ignore them. It is only a matter of time before someone is hurt. If people
have gardens they should exercise their dogs there."

However, professional dog walker and parent Melanie Croft disagrees. She volunteers in
local schools, teaching children how to stay safe around dogs. "It would be a terrible shame
if dogs were to disappear from our parks. Apart from anything else, it has been proved that   35
dog-owners tend to be healthier and live longer than people without dogs. Dog-walking is
one of the major health benefits of dog ownership. People with dogs do need to make sure
that if their dogs are let off the lead, they will behave themselves, but parents and schools
can do a lot to make sure that dogs and children can both enjoy public spaces."

It seems that while we claim to be a nation of animal lovers, our relationship with man's best   40
friend is not always so friendly. Banning dogs from our public parks, however, would be a
drastic attempt to solve problems which, after all, might better be tackled by educating dog
owners and the public alike.

Underline your answers.

1. Which of these statements is definitely true, based on the information in the text?

A child under 16 lives in almost a third of UK homes.

Dogs are just as popular as children.

There are almost as many pet dogs in the UK as there are children under 16.

Two-thirds of UK households are home to either a dog or a child under 16.

2. What does the word "menace" (line 1) mean?

manage   threat   noisy   smelly

3. What does the word "unsightly" (line 10) mean?

dangerous to eyesight   all over the place   ugly   unnecessary

4. What does the word "majority" (line 6) mean?

most   few   some   the best

5. What is "the press" (line 24)?

the playground   the dog rescue shelter   newspapers   parks   /5

Answer these questions.

6. Are you surprised by the statistics about dog numbers in the UK?
Give a reason for your answer.

_____

7–8. The text discusses two main problems with dogs being allowed in public. What are they?

_____

_____

9. Who is most at risk of toxocariasis? Underline your answer.

dog owners   dogs   16-year-olds   young children

10. Why do councils often put fences around children's play areas?

_____

11–12. What two things does the text say dog wardens are responsible for?

_____

_____

13–14. The text talks mainly about the dog-walkers and children who use the park. Write down two other groups of people who might use the park.

_____

_____

15. Why do you think some people employ a professional dog walker?

_____

16–17. Find and write down one potential health risk and one potential health benefit associated with allowing dogs in public parks.

_____

_____

18–20. Find three ways that many councils try to make parks safe places for everyone to use.

_____

_____

_____

21. Do you believe banning dogs from public spaces would "dramatically reduce" the problem of dog mess? Give a reason for your answer.

_____

_____

22. Overall, do you think that dogs should be banned from public parks? Give a reason for your answer.

_____

_____

23–24. Find and write down two words or **phrases** used in the text to introduce a change of viewpoint.

_____   _____

25. Do you agree that the UK is a nation of animal lovers? Give a reason for your answer.

_____

_____ (**/20**)

> Underline a word from the brackets that rhymes with
> the first word but has a *different* spelling pattern.

26. pour (sour, flour, floor)

27. break (beak, steak, shake)

28. great (pleat, plate, plot)

29. choose (loose, lose, moose)

30. wear (near, rare, rear)

31. toe (now, foe, grow)

32. bowl (owl, ball, roll)   (**/7**)

Add a suitable **pronoun** to complete each **sentence**.

33. I waited for Joanne but _____ was very late.

34. Although the boys were hungry, _____ saved their lunches until later.

35. We know that Mr Thomas is angry when _____ raises his voice.

36. When my little sisters are tired, _____ just want their teddies.

37. I tried to stroke the little cat but _____ scampered away.

38. Chloe and I splashed in the water until _____ were both soaking wet.

/6

Add a **colon** and **commas** to each sentence.

39–40. The table was laden with delicious foods cakes pastries and tiny sandwiches.

41–43. We saw lots of different animals at the zoo lions elephants penguins and a baby giraffe.

44–45. I have my favourite lessons today English maths and art.

/7

Underline the best **adverb** from the brackets to complete each sentence.

46. Rob (carefully, anxiously, thoroughly) painted his model.

47. The tide (calmly, sluggishly, gradually) crept up the beach.

48. The tree lent (dangerously, daringly, harmfully) over the path.

49. Nina drew her graph (nicely, accurately, decently).

50. The young children clapped (restlessly, excitedly, apprehensively) when the magician appeared.

51. Our cat jumped down (lightly, peacefully, brightly) from the garden wall.

52. (Clearly, Noisily, Silently), the class clattered down the steps and into the playground.

/7

Describe what each of these books is for, including an example of when you might use it.

53. rhyming dictionary

_____

54. encyclopaedia

_____

55. thesaurus

_____ /3

Add **speech marks** in the correct places in these sentences.

56–57. I like this one, said Sophie, holding up a blue dress.

58–59. Let's go to the beach today, suggested Dad.

60–63. I know you're busy, ventured Mark, but could you drive me to the shops? /8

Add a suitable word to complete each sentence, avoiding the word "said".

64. "This soup is cold," _____ the man, gruffly.

65. "There's a spider!" _____ Grace, leaping onto a chair.

66. "That's really funny!" _____ Anna.

67. Dad _____, "Have you seen my keys?"

68. "Get out of my room," _____ Greg, crossly.

69. "That's a pretty top," _____ Gran.

70. Jack _____, "It's not fair!" /7

/70

PAPER 10

Trapped!

Act 1

[*When the curtain rises, the stage is in darkness.*]

Tom [*concerned*]: Is everyone OK?

Mark [*crossly*]: Well that's a stupid question. We drop through a floor into goodness knows   5
where and you ask if we're OK!

Zoe: I'm fine I think. Actually, I think I landed on something soft.

Mark: [*shortly*]: You did. Me! Glad to help!

Zoe [*sarcastically*]: Well, I'm sorry! Next time a floor collapses under me I'll be more careful
where I land. Honestly Mark, you're so irritating! Don't forget whose idea it was to come to   10
this dilapidated house anyway!

Tom [*frustrated*]: Calm down, you two. Arguing isn't going to get us out of here. We all
agreed to explore the house and blaming each other won't get us anywhere.

Zoe: Tom's right, Mark. I'm sorry.

Mark [*haughtily*]: Well, fair enough then.   15

Zoe: It is so dark in here! Do you think there are spiders?

Tom: Did either of you manage to hang on to your torch?

Zoe: Oh no! I left mine up in the house, on the hall table.

Tom: Me too.

Mark: Oh, well done you two! I was holding mine when we fell. It must be here somewhere.   20

[*Shuffling sounds are heard as the children feel around for the torch*.]

Zoe: I think I have it. No, wait, it's a foot. Is that you Tom?

Tom: No, I'm over here. It must be Mark.

Mark [*worried*]: Errr, it's not me either. I'm right next to Tom.

Zoe [*speaking quickly, sounding scared*]: Well I just had hold of someone's foot so if it's not   25
one of you, who on earth was it?

Mark: I've found the torch!

Zoe [*panicking*]: Switch it on, quick! Quick!

Mark: [*desperately clicking the torch switch*]: I can't. The switch is jammed. I think it's broken!

[*Dragging footsteps are heard. Zoe shrieks. A door at the back of the stage opens, and the   30
stage is lit dimly. The three friends are revealed centre stage, looking around them for the first
time. Terrified, they realise they are alone. The curtain falls*.]

Underline your answers.

1. Which of these words is closest in meaning to the word "haughtily" (line 15)?

   roughly   quietly   scornfully   loudly

2. Which of these words is closest in meaning to the word "dilapidated" (line 11)?

   haunted   ramshackle   rambling   remote

3. Which of these words is closest in meaning to the word "irritating", as it is used in this text (line 10)?

   itchy   rude   annoying   soothing   /3

Answer these questions.

4. What has happened to the children?

   _____

   _____

5. Why is the stage in darkness?

   _____

6. Who does Zoe blame for the situation they are in?

   _____

7. Do you think this is fair? Give a reason for your answer.

   _____

   _____

8. When Zoe says she is sorry that she fell on Mark (line 9), do you think she really means it? Which word in the stage directions tells you this?

   _____

   _____

9–10. Find two other examples of dialogue that have a similar tone.

_____

_____

11. Why do you think neither Tom nor Mark respond to Zoe's question about spiders?

_____

12. Of the three characters, which do you think acts most calmly? Give a reason for your choice.

_____

_____

13. What, or who, do you think Zoe gets hold of?

_____

14. Why does she panic?

_____

15. Suggest a reason why the stage directions say that Zoe speaks quickly at this point in the script (line 25).

_____

16. Who, or what, do you think walks across the floor (line 30)?

_____

17. Where do you think the door that opens might lead?

_____

18. When the curtain rises for Act 2, do you think the children will go through the door? Give a reason for your answer.

_____

19. What is the special name for the *italic* words in square brackets?

_____

20. What is their purpose?

_____

21–23. Apart from speech, list three other sounds that are heard.

_____   _____   _____

24. Why is tone of voice so important with this particular script?

_____

25. Do you think facial expressions are more important than dialogue at any point in the script? If so, when and why?

_____

_____   /22

Underline the incorrectly spelt word in each group.

26.	genius	furius	spacious
27.	definite	agitate	favourate
28.	process	posess	caress
29.	wierd	cheaper	healthier
30.	career	appeer	beard
31.	suceed	precede	proceed
32.	thirteen	forteen	fifteen

/7

Level 5

Underline the **adjective** in each sentence.

33. My little sister is terribly disorganised.

34. A rare butterfly fluttered through the garden.

35. I did not play football because I had a sore knee.

36. The scary film was totally terrifying.

37. "You're such a lucky girl!" said Mum, paying for the shoes.

38. Dad was furious when we broke the antique vase.

39. The azure sea glistened brightly in the sunshine.

/7

Write these sentences again, with the correct **punctuation**.

40–41. I put ham; lettuce; cucumber and tomato in my sandwich.

_____

42–43. Although its bad for you if you eat too much I do love ice-cream!

_____

44–45. Your room is a disgrace, complained Mum.

_____

46–48. "Why are you late! asked Mrs Bridges, looking at the clock

_____

/9

Complete these **similes** in an original way.

49. as white as _____

50. as old as _____

51. as big as _____

/3

Add suitable words to turn these **phrases** into complete **sentences**.

52. large green bag

_____

53. to the library

_____

54. across the road

_____

55. crept quietly

_____

56. thick, heavy book

_____

57. difficult game

_____

58. in the sea

_____　　/7

Write a sentence explaining one way each punctuation mark is used. Then write a second sentence showing an example.

59–60. comma

_____

_____

61–62. semi-colon

_____

_____

63–64. apostrophe

_____

_____ /6

Underline the word that *does not* belong in each group.

65. **verbs**	mend	bawl	river	rest
66. **nouns**	ring	badly	block	fortune
67. **prepositions**	very	on	under	beside
68. **adjectives**	blue	blew	soft	huge
69. **adverbs**	slowly	badly	cruel	warmly
70. **pronouns**	them	the	we	it

/6

/70

Glossary

active verb	a verb where the subject of the sentence is the main focus, e.g. *The man ate the apple*.
adjective	a word that describes a noun, e.g. *tiny*, *green*
adverb	a word that describes a verb, e.g. *kindly*, *stupidly*
alliteration	a phrase where two or more words begin with the same sound, e.g. *one wonderful weekend*
apostrophe	a punctuation mark used to show possession or contraction, e.g. *Amy's pen* (the pen belonging to Amy), *I'll* (I will)
clause	a part of a sentence that contains a verb. See also main clause and subordinate clause.
colon	a punctuation mark used to introduce a list, quotation or a second clause which adds information to the first, e.g. *For our picnic we bought: French bread, cheese, strawberries and bananas.*
comma	a punctuation mark used to separate parts of a sentence. They are used in particular to separate clauses or items in a list, e.g. *Although it was sunny, we packed an umbrella. The boys ate sandwiches, crisps, cakes and fruit.*
comparative adjective	an adjective used to compare degrees of the same quality in two different things, e.g. *smaller, better*
complex sentence	a sentence that contains a main clause and a subordinate clause, e.g. *The mouse will escape if you do not close its cage.*
connective	a word or words that join clauses or sentences, e.g. *and, but, however*
direct speech	the actual words that someone has said, indicated using speech marks, e.g. *"Where is the library?", asked Joe.*
imperative verb	verbs that tell you to do something, e.g. *Glue section B to section C.*
main clause	the main part of a sentence that makes sense on its own, e.g. *I'll get wet if it rains.*
noun	a word that names a thing or a feeling, e.g. *football, love*
object	The person or thing that a verb relates to in a sentence, e.g. *Lisa sang a song*.
onomatopoeia	a word that makes the sound that it describes, e.g. *bang*
paragraph	a section of a piece of writing, used to organise information. A new paragraph indicates a change in topic, place, time or speaker.
passive verb	a verb where the object of the sentence is the focus, e.g. *The nut was eaten by the squirrel.*

personification	where non-human things are described as having human qualities, e.g. *The sun smiled on us*.
phrase	two or more words which act together as a unit, e.g. *a black cat*
plural	more than one of something, e.g. *books, mice, children*
preposition	a word that describes the position of one thing in relation to another, e.g. *on*, *under*, *from*
pronoun	a word that can be used in the place of a noun, e.g. *I, you, she, they*
punctuation	marks used in writing to help the reader, e.g. *comma*, *full stop*, *apostrophe*, *semi-colon*
reported speech	what someone has said, without their actual words being used, e.g. *Our teacher told us to pack our things away.*
semi-colon	a punctuation mark used to separate clauses or phrases in a sentence, e.g. *We were too late; the train had already left.*
sentence	a unit of written language that makes sense on its own. Sentences start with a capital letter and end with a full-stop, question mark or exclamation mark, e.g. *Did you see him?*
simile	where one thing is compared to another using the word 'as' or 'like', e.g. *as old as the hills*
speech marks	punctuation marks used to indicate direct speech, e.g. *"Stop!" shouted Mark.*
subordinate clause	adds more information to a main clause, but does not make sense on its own, e.g. *I will phone you <u>when</u> I <u>get</u> <u>back</u>.*
subject	the person (or thing) who carries out the verb in a sentence, e.g. <u>*Lisa*</u> *sang a song.*
superlative adjective	an adjective used to describe the fullest possible extent of a particular quality, e.g. *smallest, best*
tense	convention used to show whether a verb is in the past, present or future, e.g. *I walked, I walk, I will walk*
verb	a doing or being word, e.g. *we <u>walk</u>, you <u>swim</u>, I <u>am</u>*

Progress grid

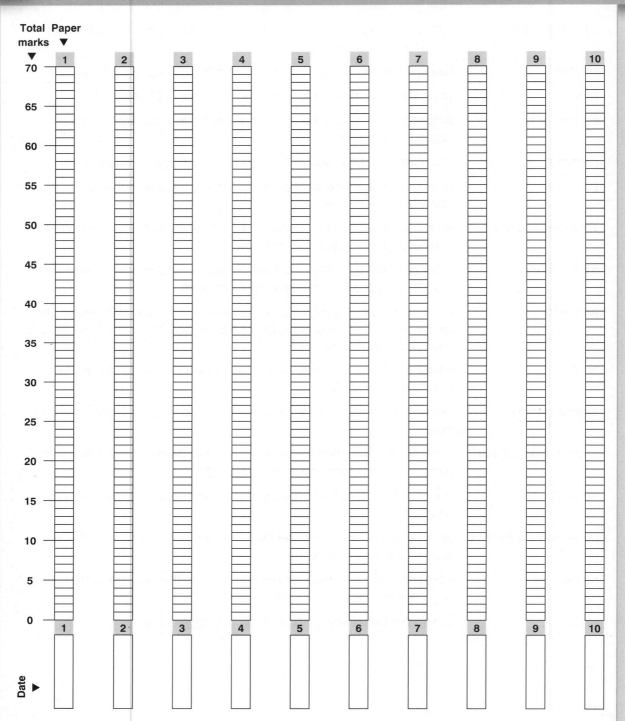

Total marks ▼
Paper ▼

Date ▶

Now colour in your score!